The Sober Survival Guide

How to free yourself from alcohol forever

by Simon Chapple

Join the alcohol-free movement at: www.besober.co.uk
Reach out: info@besober.co.uk

Find Be Sober on Instagram and Facebook: @besoberandquit

If you like to share:
Upload a picture of yourself with your copy of *The Sober Survival Guide* on Instagram. Follow and tag @besoberandquit in your picture so I can follow you back and join you on your journey to alcohol freedom - Simon.

Contents

Foreword by Annie Grace

I met Simon Chapple in a video chat room when he joined This Naked Mind podcast to tell his story. I was immediately struck by Simon's passion for the sober life. Not only had he overcome any desire to drink, he was *thriving.* He was proud. He was excited. And he was passionate. And he was paying it forward.

Simon had already started an incredible online group, Be Sober, and members were flocking to his joyful and encouraging approach. It was not long after that amazing meeting that I asked Simon to come to the United States and be trained to be the first This Naked Mind Certified Coach in the UK.

Meeting Simon IRL (In Real Life!) surpassed all my expectations. He was the same kind, genuine and outrageously passionate person. It was a joy to spend the week together, train him to be a coach, and watch, as he has now coached thousands of people along the journey to what he has termed 'Alcohol Freedom'.

Hearing that Simon had written a book was no surprise. When I read it, I was awed by the combination of raw, honest storytelling with practical, tangible tips for finding true joy and freedom without alcohol.

You have in your hands The Guide to letting go of alcohol and maybe even more importantly, to life after putting down the bottle. The map to exuberance, self-care, and true freedom in an alcohol-free lifestyle. I hope you enjoy this book as much as I did.

Love, Annie Grace
This Naked Mind: Control Alcohol, Find Freedom, Discover Happiness & Change Your Life

Annie Grace authored *This Naked Mind: Control Alcohol, Find Freedom, Discover Happiness & Change Your Life*. Her book reprograms your unconscious, allowing you to break free from alcohol. Countless hours of research went into writing the book, which breaks down how alcohol changes us both physically and mentally.

Annie no longer drinks and has never been happier. She left her executive role to write the book and share her method with the world. Since publishing her book she has featured in publications such as *Forbes*, *New York Daily News*, *The Chicago Tribune* and *Mind Body Green*. Annie Grace wants to share her message and the ability to find freedom from alcohol with as many readers as possible. Beyond the book, her goal is to reshape society's views and our alcoholcentric culture so that the non-drinker is no longer an exception to the rule.

You can discover more about This Naked Mind and Annie's work by visiting **www.thisnakedmind.com**

 THIS NAKED MIND

Introduction

Hands up if you believe any of the following about drinking alcohol to be true:

- I can't have fun without it. Imagine going to a party without drinking!
- It makes me feel less anxious or depressed.
- It helps me sleep.
- I can't relax without it.
- It makes me entertaining to be around.
- It fits the lifestyle of my boozy friends.
- I like the taste.
- It's cool and sophisticated.
- I'm not confident enough to talk to new people without it.
- It helps me deal with all the problems that life throws my way.
- It stops me from worrying, especially about how much I'm drinking (ironic, I know).

If you find yourself nodding at even one of these statements, then I know how you feel. I too used to believe that I couldn't live without alcohol, and that once I'd had a few drinks, I was funny to be around (hilarious, in fact). Being honest, I was a heavy daily drinker for well over twenty years.

Slowly, I reached the point at which I felt sick and tired of feeling sick and tired. I became fed up with the hangovers, the regretful behaviour (there was enough of that to write another book about!) and the damage alcohol was causing my relationships, my career, my body, and my mind (to say nothing of my soul). I started to see that the beliefs I listed above were wrong: alcohol was no longer serving me or adding anything positive to my life. In fact, it had been stealing my happiness and wellbeing for years, and I decided I wanted what it had stolen back.

From this point on, it took me a full five years to face up to my problem and find the key to transforming my life. Because alcohol is so addictive, it was doing exactly what it was designed to do: get me hooked on it, so I felt I couldn't give up. How on earth was I going to haul myself out of the hole I'd dug for myself, and which I'd been stuck in for so long? It was obvious I was a problem drinker, but what should I do now? This uncertainty led me to dig myself even further into the ground by drinking more so that I would stop thinking about it. I just wanted the painful thoughts to leave my head, and wine seemed the perfect solution.

However, I did eventually remove the grip that alcohol had on me and have gone on to live a life of complete happiness ever since. I learned that what I'd believed about alcohol was completely wrong. Of course, I didn't understand this at the beginning, but as I steadily moved down the path to alcohol freedom, everything became so very clear.

You may be reading this book because you too are tired and fed up with the routine of drinking, and you want to make a change and improve your life. Or you may simply be curious about how a life without alcohol might look for you. Could it be better? Happier? Calmer? More peaceful? Perhaps you're already on the path to changing your relationship with booze and might have read other 'sober books' or taken part in programmes to help you quit.

I want you to know that you can do the same as me, and you don't have to wait for years like I did. Also, I want to reassure you that addiction is never a person's fault, and that there's no need to blame yourself for finding it hard to give up. It honestly isn't as hard as you might think, and this book will provide the support and advice you need as you progress on your sober journey.

You may have heard of the word 'sober' and assume it simply describes someone who doesn't drink. But sobriety is so much more than that. For me, it's a lifestyle – a way of living due to a choice I made that led me on a wonderful journey of self-improvement, awareness, and wellbeing. So when you read my thoughts on sobriety in this book, I'm not just talking about it as simply quitting drinking. On the contrary, to 'go sober' is to embark on an amazing adventure during which you'll discover a whole new version of yourself.

For me, that's included launching one of the world's fastest-growing online sober communities. I also work as a coach helping people who want to change their relationship with alcohol, and have spoken at live events and become an enthusiastic advocate of the sober movement (we're not alone). This means that I've helped thousands of people to explore how alcohol fits into their life, and many of them have chosen to quit drinking altogether.

Now, through this book, my hope is that I can do the same for you. By the end of it, you should see how you can be free to make your own choices about how you drink and you will feel equipped to decide whether you want to do it any longer. It's up to you. Don't waste time like I did – take action now.

How to use this book

The book is split into two parts. The first is designed to set you up for success and put you in a place where you can find freedom from alcohol, if that's what you want. It's important that you read this all the way through, as it contains essential information for when you're in the early stages of controlling your drinking.

The second part serves as a handbook as you move forward into an alcohol-free life and this is, if I'm honest, where this book comes into its own. As you read it you'll see that I've used my own experiences and those of the people I've worked with to help ensure you're ready for the challenges, fears, and questions that will come up in the years after you've quit drinking. You'll learn how to handle the work Christmas party without a glass of bubbly in hand, the joys of sober holidays, what to do when you stop drinking but your partner won't, and a whole lot more. With this part, you can dip in and out, picking the chapters that address the problems you're facing that particular day or week.

At this point, it's important to be clear that this book isn't a replacement for professional medical advice. If you're physically addicted to alcohol, or experiencing severe withdrawal symptoms, such as shaking, tremors, hallucinations, or any other side effects that cause you concern, please visit your doctor and get medical advice. However, if you're either ready to start thinking about what a life without alcohol might look like, or have already given up and are looking for further support and tactics as you move forward on your alcohol-free journey, this book is for you. Either way, you have found the perfect companion to help you on the path to complete freedom.

Let's take some positive action. Read on and start learning how to change your life in the most incredible and positive ways.

I am Simon Chapple and I am an ~~alcoholic~~

Actually, no. I am Simon Chapple and I don't drink alcohol.

Why do I describe myself like this? Because I don't feel I should carry a label for the rest of my life. I'm now free from the grip of alcohol and I don't drink – it's that simple. You don't need to carry a label either; you can choose whatever works for you. Some people like to use the term 'alcoholic' to help keep them focused, but for me, it doesn't fit and is not one I care to use.

I am also not in 'recovery', which sounds like I have an injury or am suffering from an illness. This word suggests I'm not 100 percent fit and healthy, which is wrong. Since I cut alcohol out of my life I've become the best version of myself I've ever been, along with finding true happiness, peace, and new levels of calm. I'm not in recovery, I'm free!

Alcohol is the only drug in the world that we seem to have to justify not taking. When someone quits smoking they're congratulated on the achievement, not referred to as a 'cigarette-aholic' who is 'in recovery from tobacco'. But when we stop drinking we're often met with some strange reactions from people, and on top of this, we're assigned the labels I've mentioned. Alcoholism still carries a huge stigma. However, I've been working hard to change social attitudes and preconceptions, and as the sober revolution gathers force and more and more people realise that a life without alcohol is the best choice, the tide is starting to turn.

Remember that you hold the power to be who you want to be, and you can choose what labels you use for yourself. Alcohol does not have to define you as a person.

Alcohol and me

I drank alcohol every day for as long as I can remember – it was a love affair that lasted the best part of 30 years. My habit started when I was around 14 years old and started to notice how my dad would drink red wine at home; I'd look up to him with admiration, thinking how cool, mature, and sophisticated it seemed. I remember he drank a posh French red wine called Beaujolais Nouveau. Like most teenagers, I thought the world of my dad and wanted to emulate him; to me, that meant drinking grown-up wine, just like he did.

I was an only child and we lived in a small, semi-detached house in a military town called Aldershot, around 20 miles south of London, England. My dad used to run his own courier business, but he never really made it big and always seemed to fall short of achieving his dreams. He had an amazing ability when it came to attracting bad luck, and we never had much money (although now I'm older and wiser, I realise he actually brought a lot of that misfortune on himself through the impulsive decisions he made).

But it didn't make me love him any less – in fact, I admired the way he never gave up. I thought it was amazing that he had his own business, no matter how up and down it was. He was a solid rock for me, especially during my turbulent teenage years, which were one swirling mass (or should I say mess) of hormones, girls, school, and worries about what people thought of me.

My mum was, and still is, wonderful and supportive of everything I do. But she's always been a natural-born worrier, and from an early age, I can remember her convincing me that danger and death awaited this little boy around every corner. I firmly believe that the 'worry' elements of the anxiety that would go on to affect me, were a direct result of her over-protective nature. However, she was only looking out for me and I haven't run into any danger or death yet, so thanks mum, you did a good job.

As an only child, mum and dad were huge influences on my life. We had family meals almost every day and when I was around 14, after badgering my dad for weeks and weeks, he started to let me have a glass of red wine with my dinner. At first, I thought it tasted awful (of course it did, it was poison and my body was sending me a message not to put it inside myself, just as if I'd eaten food that had gone off), but I ignored the warnings and soon developed a taste for the wine. This evolved into me being allowed to take the remains of the bottle up to my bedroom. Before long, I was getting my hands on my own alcohol and starting to rely on it to numb feelings of sadness, loneliness, and of course, the dreaded dark clouds of anxiety that were starting to take over my life.

Around the same time, my small group of friends and I decided to see if we could get served in the local pub called The Beehive. With Aldershot being an army town, they were used to fresh-faced boys coming in so we used the cover story of being new army recruits. I remember how nervous I was as we approached the door, as well as the smell of stale beer and smoke hanging in the air outside. I had visions of us being turned away and laughed out of the bar, but we walked in and tried to look like confident lads who were simply out for a few beers. To my amazement, we were served without any question. I'd never had a 'proper' pint before and was surprised at how big it was in my hand, but I gulped it down like it was water and was soon back at the bar ordering my next. We ended up visiting The Beehive a few nights a week for years, and it became our drinking haunt. I wonder if the landlord ever wondered why we didn't get posted away with our military unit?

At every pub visit, one pint always quickly became more, and I would feel myself relaxing as the alcohol took effect. It was almost a euphoric experience, and my anxiety and worries faded into the background. I was laughing and having so much fun with my friends

– clearly this was what being grown up was all about. Maybe I'd found the answer to my problems after all. I only ever drank beer in pubs, probably because I thought it was macho. I would usually work my way through four to six pints in an evening (often with some shots of straight whisky or vodka to wash it down) and then stagger my way home and start on the wine. I always had to have the wine, no matter what. Looking back, I was on a slippery slope even in my mid to late teens.

When I reached 17, I left school and landed a job as an office junior in town. I couldn't wait to move into the big wide world, and I loved putting on my business suit and feeling like I was on the path to making it big. My mum and I worked for different businesses that were close to each other, and we would walk to our respective offices together each morning. Our strolls were a lovely opportunity to talk one-on-one and enjoy each other's company. One day, however, mum received terrible news out of the blue; the insurance company where she'd worked as a typist for years was closing and she would be made redundant. This hit her hard, and knowing how much she habitually worried about things, I can only imagine the turmoil it caused her. She ended up sinking into depression and suffering a nervous breakdown, which put a huge strain on our family.

Fast-forward to the age of 25. I had two failed relationships behind me and was still working in the same insurance job that I'd been in since I left school, which had long since lost its shine. I'd met the girl of my dreams (Michelle, who I'm proud to say is now my wife) and we decided to move into our first home together. When I announced this to my parents, they told me the very next day they were getting divorced and they'd been living separate lives for years but hadn't wanted to break up for my sake (I often wondered why dad slept in the spare bedroom, and now it was clear). They'd waited all this time and put on a show just for my benefit, but why hadn't they just parted company when they wanted to and been happy instead?

This was heartbreaking for me, and I spent days crying like a baby. So what did I do? I drank more to blot it out and numb the pain. This was the point at which my drinking became even heavier, and I struggle to remember a single day between then and when I was 44 years old when I didn't have at least a bottle of red wine a night. In fact, just about the only times I can remember not drinking was when I was sick with the flu and when I was forced to spend the night in hospital after an operation. It says a lot about the level of power that alcohol had over me that before the procedure, I was more apprehensive about not having any wine than I was about going through the ordeal of surgery.

Unless I was physically unable to lay my hands on my wine, I would drink. It was always there for me, like a faithful friend, never leaving my side. It was the true constant in my life, and I was now deep into an unhealthy relationship with alcohol and totally unaware I was heading down a dark and dangerous rabbit hole. In 2004, Michelle and I had a daughter, but I was never truly happy. I loved them both but there was a void in my life that I couldn't put my finger on or explain. I felt like I was evolving into a sad, grumpy old man, but I assumed that was just who I was. Maybe I should accept it.

My anxiety also became worse. Michelle and I had started our own business, a marketing company which we still run today, and the anxiety had grown so bad that I could no longer bear to go into the office. The slightest issue with a staff member, or a client making a complaint would result in me having a meltdown. I'd wind myself into a complete state with irrational worries about the slightest little thing. This led me to visit doctors, counsellors, and even a hypnotherapist. None of them helped me much, nor did they explore my drinking habits or suggest cutting alcohol out of my life. One doctor asked how much I drank as a routine question, but of course I lied (don't we all? I've since learned that doctors routinely double the figure they're told by their patients to gain a true picture of their drinking habits – we heavy drinkers are excellent liars).

Sadly, I also fell out with my dad over a petty argument, and we haven't spoken or seen each other for over five years. I often wonder what part my state of mind due to alcohol had to play in that. I would dearly love to heal the past and share my story with him as I think he would be incredibly proud of what I've achieved, so if you ever read this book dad, take these words as the olive branch of peace.

The result was that I took the decision to step away and take some much-needed time out, which I felt awful about as we had over 20 staff and hundreds of clients who required constant managing. Michelle had to run things on her own, but she was supportive of me and knew I needed space to deal with my anxiety issues. It was during this break that I started looking more closely at my relationship with alcohol, and became curious about what my life might look like if I could ever stop drinking. Whenever I started to consider the vision of an alcohol-free life the thought of not being able to drink, even for just one day, put a knot in my stomach. It seemed ridiculous and unachievable, but my mind kept nudging away at me and saying, 'something needs to change'.

And then it did...

The big change

During my quest to explore my drinking, I came across the book *This Naked Mind* by Annie Grace, which was based on a 30-day experiment that Annie had designed to help readers understand the effects of alcohol and to question their own relationships with it. What did I have to lose? I bought myself a copy and after the first chapter was hooked (I've discovered that I have a strange habit of getting hooked on things, so I'm now mindful about what I get myself into). If you haven't read *This Naked Mind*, I recommend doing so; the term 'game-changer' was an understatement for me. I have so much to thank Annie for; her work has helped to change the lives of thousands of people (including my own) and she's been at the forefront of the sober revolution with her non-judgmental and practical approach to changing the way people view alcohol.

I read the book twice in a row and then started watching videos about sobriety, joining online sober groups, and learning everything I could about living a life without alcohol. I found this new sober world fascinating and exciting. However, even though I was on the right track, success didn't come straight away – nor was I expecting it to. It took quite a bit of hard work, but I firmly believed that I would get out what I put in. It was obvious to me that I needed to keep educating myself and working on my beliefs; in fact, I approached it like I was studying for the most important exam of my life. Each day would find me making notes and voice recordings, and even starting to blog about my journey on my website. These activities helped me to express my thoughts and feelings in a structured way, and an unexpected benefit of my blog is that I can now look back on what I have learned, comparing notes with what I know now.

After two months of daily reading, watching videos, and journaling about sobriety, I could feel a slow change starting to emerge. It was as if my mind no longer wanted me to drink as a default activity, and there was a new pathway forming. Somehow, I knew there would be something incredible waiting for me at the end of it. Of course, there were odd days when I started to feel bored of reading about sobriety, but I wanted to learn about it so badly that I pushed through.

Then one day I realised I was experiencing a mindset shift from 'I can't have a drink' to 'I don't want one'. This felt incredibly liberating. My beliefs about alcohol were changing: drinking started to become unimportant and I didn't want booze around me any longer. I found myself in a place of complete freedom and peace. Even then, the transformation wasn't without its hiccups – there were a few false starts and a couple of teary meltdowns. But I managed to put myself on the path to sobriety, which felt so exciting.

The very first day I put the bottle down, I took a selfie and after a few weeks, took another to compare them. The difference in my face, skin, and eyes was incredible! The dark shadows had disappeared, I was no longer bloated, and my skin was positively glowing. This spurred me on, because I figured if this much had changed on the outside in such a short space of time, imagine what was going on inside.

As time went by, the dark clouds of anxiety that had hung over me for years started to fade and I could see the sun starting to shine through. I even questioned what was going on, as I hadn't felt this good in years. After all, I'd only quit drinking because I didn't want to die before the age of 50 – I'd never expected to experience a whole new lease of life on top. And guess what? The anxiety has never returned. It felt like a toxic relationship had come to an end, one that should have finished years ago. Now I could see how much better my life was without the constant cycle of drinking and its associated behaviours and side effects, there was no way I was going to return to my old ways. It was over.

At the same time as starting the *Be Sober* blog, I decided to launch a Facebook group for other people who wanted to explore their relationship with alcohol. I'd already participated in several of these, but I specifically wanted to create something with a friendly and personal feel where members could reach out for support and know that they had a trusting and caring community around them. I also felt quite lonely on my journey, so when people started asking to join the group it showed me there were thousands of others in the same boat.

My Facebook group is now one of the largest online sober communities in the world, with thousands of members supporting each other while working to change their relationship with alcohol. If you'd like to join the group you'd be welcomed with open arms; just visit www.besober.co.uk for the link or search 'Be Sober' on Facebook. I love reading the posts and comments from the group members, because they're so inspirational and heart-warming. Later in the book, I'll share some of my favourites, to add a real-world perspective to the challenges that arise in sobriety.

As my blog started to grow, I thought it would be great to ask Annie Grace for an interview; after all, it was her book that had changed my life. To my amazement, she agreed and the conversation was great fun even if I was a little starstruck (you can watch it on the Be Sober website). After the interview, Annie asked me if I'd thought about becoming an alcohol coach, and would I be interested in joining her team at This Naked Mind, her sober coaching business. I'd made one change in my life by cutting out alcohol, and now more doors were opening for me on the back of it! After I'd pinched myself, to check it wasn't a dream, I agreed, and before long I was on a plane to America to start training as a coach with Annie and her team.

I've now become a Senior Coach at This Naked Mind, I've talked at the This Naked Mind Live event in Denver, Colorado, and I even help train new coaches. Through this I've helped thousands of people to change the way they think about drinking and to quit for good, enabling them to become truly free from the grip of alcohol.

The journey to sobriety can seem scary and confusing and you might be worried about which direction to take and what strategies to use. I wrote this book by drawing on my own experiences to help you as you go forward. It's like a map and compass to ensure you find your way to alcohol freedom without getting lost or ending back at the start. In fact, one of the resources I wish I'd had back then was a book that advised me on the specific problems and challenges I faced after I made the decision to give up the drink; those meltdowns would have been a lot easier to deal with if I'd known what they were caused by, and what to do about them. There are plenty of books that help you get off the booze as a first step, but I couldn't find any that would set me up and hold my hand for the challenges I faced in the months, years and lifetime ahead.

But enough about me – let's get started.

Part One

The first part of this book sets the scene for you to explore what an alcohol-free life might look like for you. It will also help you to look closely at your relationship with drinking and your beliefs about how it serves your life.

Please read all the chapters here; you can dip in and out of the ones in Part Two if you like, but in this section, you need it all – trust me.

Chapter 1
What you need to know about alcohol

Over 90 percent of people in the Western World drink alcohol, and sadly over two million of them a year die as a direct result. Just pause and think about that number; over the course of a decade, 20 million people end up dead because of drinking. If alcohol had never existed and someone invented it today, I'm pretty sure it would never reach the shops.

Picture the scene. The inventor of this incredible new drink called 'alcohol' is sat in a dark, smoky bar, pitching his new invention to unsuspecting customers. 'I've come up with this amazing new drink – go on, have a glass. It makes you lose your inhibitions, do dangerous and regrettable things, and forget you did them afterwards. You'll also become emotional, argumentative, and violent. The next day you'll almost certainly feel sick and ill, but you'll still crave more of it because it's incredibly addictive. If you drink it consistently over time, there's a good chance you'll damage your physical and mental health and maybe even lose your job, home, and family. It might even kill you in the end.' Would you take a sip? I don't think so. And yet this stuff is available to buy right now – I like to call it 'cleverly packaged poison'.

Of the small amount of people who don't drink, only a small percentage are sober because of making a conscious choice that alcohol isn't for them. This is how deeply ingrained drinking is in our culture, to the point where many people think you're slightly odd if you don't drink. Very few consider alcohol to be a drug, even though it's among the most harmful and addictive substances in the world. It's considered socially acceptable and the 'done thing' in most countries. In fact, where I live in the UK you generally have to give some kind of justification not to drink. Imagine having to do that with heroin or cocaine!

On top of this, we live in a world which is dominated by a multi-billion dollar marketing industry dedicated to promoting the 'benefits' of alcohol on television and radio, in newspapers, on billboards, and on social media. It's inevitable that we become brainwashed to join in the 'fun'. I've even seen an advert that aligned a low-calorie beer with sporting activities to give a sense that drinking beer is part of a healthy lifestyle. Alcohol manufacturers push every boundary they can because they want you to believe that if you buy their products you'll end up blissfully happy, with the perfect partner, in a perfect house, and successful in everything you do. This is far from the truth, and I'm surprised at how far some of their commercials are allowed to go.

Of course, many people can drink moderately and know when to stop. But for others, it can be an all or nothing affair. Whenever I do anything I have to dive in with both feet, and wine was no exception. If you've found that alcohol is running the show and you're putting it ahead of important things in your life, such as your relationships, work, friends, family, exercise, and health, then it's probably time to start questioning your drinking. Alcohol is sly and creeps up on you. It starts out as fun, but over time, it takes away more than it gives back – without exception. Every time we have a drinking session we end up worse off than when we started, and the slope becomes more and more slippery until we've travelled so far down it, we think we can't get back up it again. So what do we do? We have another drink of course.

What alcohol does to your body

We can see what alcohol does to our lives, but what does it do to our bodies? In reality, it starts to affect them as soon as we take our first sip, so it's important to understand the damage it can cause. I often speak to heavy drinkers who believe that because they've never encountered any of the issues outlined below they're fine to continue drinking, almost as if the science and facts don't apply to them. But just because the problems haven't arisen yet, doesn't mean they won't; none of us is immune. This denial is a way of settling our minds when we start to have uncomfortable thoughts about our drinking habits.

The fact is that alcohol is a poison called ethanol or ethyl alcohol. You'll find ethanol in cleaning products, motor fuel (ethanol has also been used as a rocket fuel), solvents, and numerous household and commercial products that I'm sure you would never consider drinking. Below is a list of the main areas of your body that can be impacted when you regularly drink alcohol (or ethanol).

Your skin
If you want to look ten years older, become a heavy drinker. Have you ever looked at someone and immediately realised they're a boozer just from their face?

Due to the dehydration alcohol causes, your skin can become dry, wrinkled, and lacking in natural colour. Heavy drinking also causes a loss of collagen and elasticity in the skin, ageing it artificially. In my coaching, I encourage people to take before and after selfies, and they almost always look years younger once their skin has had time to recover and become rehydrated.

Heavy drinking can also lead to red and blotchy skin. Studies have shown that this is often due to the body taking longer than it should to break down the compounds of the toxin acetaldehyde in the alcohol. This means the toxins stay in the body for longer than normal, creating a serious risk of high blood pressure which, in turn, increases the chances of a heart attack or stroke.

Your brain

The moment alcohol enters your body it starts to affect your brain. It can cause short-term effects, such as:

- memory loss;
- lack of judgement;
- poor motor control and reflexes;
- loss of inhibition, and
- changes in mood.

Drinking heavily over the longer-term can cause further problems, including:

- serious memory problems, including the inability to retain and form new memories;
- lack of cognitive function that can impact on almost every area including speech, vision and hearing;
- inability to concentrate or focus;
- behavioural problems;
- increased anxiety;
- depression, and
- addiction – I know this seems obvious, but with continued exposure to alcohol, your brain becomes dependent on the drug. It craves more and more of it, which can lead to withdrawal symptoms if you stop and make it hard to resist the urge to take another drink.

This is by no means a comprehensive list of the damage alcohol can cause to your brain; scientists are still discovering more about the long-term dangers of ethanol.

Cancer

It's a fact that alcohol significantly increases your chances of developing cancer, especially of the mouth, throat, bowel, stomach, colon, and oesophagus. If you're a woman your chances of breast cancer are dramatically increased if you have a heavy drinking habit.

Your heart
Alcohol is clearly linked to high blood pressure, also called hypertension. Over time, the raised pressure causes strain on your heart muscle, which increases the risk of a heart attack or stroke.

Your liver
The liver processes around 90 percent of the alcohol you consume. If you drink heavily it can struggle to function properly, becoming unable to filter and remove harmful substances. You might have heard of how resilient livers are, being able to regenerate themselves, but the fact is that every time you drink alcohol some of your liver cells die. With prolonged heavy drinking, your liver can lose its ability to fully regenerate – and you only have the one. You can also end up with numerous liver-related health issues, including fatty liver, alcoholic hepatitis, and cirrhosis.

Your lungs
Alcohol kills some of the good bacteria that live in your throat and mouth, leaving room for unwanted bacteria to multiply. Regular heavy drinking, therefore, leaves you more susceptible to serious illnesses and respiratory problems, including pneumonia, tuberculosis, asthma, and sepsis.

Your stomach
Alcohol encourages your stomach to produce more acid than usual, which can irritate your entire digestive system. The acid can cause the lining of your stomach to become inflamed (gastritis), leading to stomach pains, diarrhoea, vomiting, and even bleeding.

Your fertility
If you're a man, heavy drinking is proven to increase the chance of erectile dysfunction. It can also lead to a low sperm count and therefore contribute towards infertility. If you're a woman who

drinks a lot, you can suffer from fertility and menstrual problems. And we all know that drinking during pregnancy can lead to long-term damage to the baby.

Your bones
Regular drinking can increase the risk of thinning bones (osteoporosis) because your stomach can't absorb the amount of calcium and vitamin D it needs for healthy bone density and growth.

Your muscles
Alcohol prevents the smooth flow of calcium through the muscle cells, which is responsible for making them contract naturally. This can cause muscle pain or cramps, as well as a feeling of weakness in your muscles.

Your weight
Alcoholic drinks are full of empty calories, so heavy drinking is a great way to pile on the pounds.

Your eyes
When you drink regularly you don't experience refreshing and restorative sleep (even though you may not realise it). As well as causing a lack of energy, it also makes you look tired. Dark shadows under the eyes are common in heavy drinkers.

Bloatedness
When you drink, your body tries to hang on to as much water as possible and this causes bloating. It can affect your face, body, hands, and feet, and make them look swollen.

Your hair and nails
These can become brittle when you drink regularly, and studies have even shown that alcohol can cause hair loss.

Your teeth and tongue

If you drink red wine, like I did, you'll be familiar with the purple 'morning tongue' that never seems to fade even after brushing your teeth multiple times. On top of this, red wine and coloured drinks can stain and damage your teeth.

Your smell

Alcohol stinks and that's a fact. When you've been drinking (including the morning after) people will be able to smell it on your breath and often on your skin as it seeps from your pores. I used to spend hours trying to hide the smell and appear 'normal'.

On top of all of this, alcohol is directly linked to many mental and physical health problems, from anxiety and depression through to cancer and ultimately death. It is also highly addictive, so there's no need to blame yourself if you feel hooked. That's what's meant to happen – it's what alcohol is designed to do.

Have you experienced any of the issues above, or been worried about them? Jot down a list. I know I used to be paranoid about damaging my liver and was self-conscious about people smelling alcohol on me when I was at work. Pause for a moment and ask yourself if you're happy to continue drinking a substance that has been proven to cause this kind of damage. I'm pretty confident the answer will be 'no', even if you're not sure how to stop drinking at this stage.

The good news is that the tide appears to be turning and recent reports suggest that as many as a third of young people are now not drinking regularly, with more and more of them deciding that a life without alcohol is the right choice. Drinking is usually a learned behaviour, as it was for me when I saw my dad drink. If the younger generation can have a different attitude towards alcohol then everyone else can as well. The fact that you're reading this book means you're probably already aware you have a problem; this is a significant step because you're on the right path and taking positive action.

However, becoming aware of a problem can be painful. It's natural to feel worried if you know something is wrong but you don't know how to fix it. That's where this book comes in, with the advice you need so that you can learn how to move from the initial stage of awareness of the issue, through to discovering how to solve it. The day can come when you've mastered the art of living a sober and happy life, in which alcohol no longer features, I promise you.

And if you've already quit drinking (well done!), please use this book as your companion and go-to solution for anything that arises in the months, years and lifetime ahead. It aims to help you through the common challenges.

In a later chapter, I'll explore how helpful keeping a journal is on your journey. But for now, all I'd like you to do is grab a notebook and reflect on your answers to the following questions:

What are your drinking habits now? How much? How often? What drinks do you have?

What were your drinking habits one year ago?

What were your drinking habits five years ago?

Compare your answers and think about your drinking trajectory. If you're like almost all the people I work with, you'll find you're drinking more now than you were before – that's how sly alcohol is. Did you give it a thought until now?

Quitting drinking means being mindful and staying aware of your behaviours, habits, beliefs, feelings, thoughts, and emotions. As you move through the book, I'll arm you with the tools and tactics you need to start bringing them out into the open so that you can work towards making a lasting change.

Chapter 2
Am I an alcoholic?

If we *have* to use the word 'alcoholic', my view is that most people who drink could be labelled as alcoholics to one degree or another – it's a spectrum. As an example, my wife drinks a bottle or two of Prosecco a week, and when I asked her if she could live a life without alcohol she replied, 'No way'. So although she's only a moderate drinker, she's still adamant that she has to have alcohol in her life to some extent. It's therefore only logical to assume that she's on that spectrum somewhere (albeit at the low end of it).

When I became aware that I had a problem with alcohol I used to search Google for answers to questions like, 'Am I an alcoholic?' and 'Am I drinking too much?' I was looking for information that would prove to me that my drinking habits were normal and I was therefore fine. Have you ever done that? For instance, I also used to look at the recommended drinking guidelines for different countries. I discovered that Spain was the most liberal in Europe, so I decided that because I have a good diet (well, I like paella) and have been to Spain on holiday a few times, I would use their guidelines instead of the stingy UK ones. What did those boffins know anyway? 'They're always over-cautious when it comes to guidelines, so I'm sure they can be taken with a pinch of salt.'

Of course, I stretched them to breaking point, drinking four or five times what even the Spanish alcohol guidelines laid out. This was in aid of settling my mind, which was in turmoil about what I was drinking. One half was telling me I needed to quit, and the other was saying I needed to keep on drinking as it was the only way to have fun, be happy, and calm my anxiety. On top of this, the thought of even one day without my beloved wine filled me with a sense of absolute dread.

On top of stretching the drinking guidelines as far as I could, I also made sure that my Facebook and Instagram feeds only showed me posts that reinforced my belief that alcohol was not a problem for me. I followed my favourite wine brands and bars, and I always liked and commented on posts telling me that wine was good for the heart or how alcohol was the key to having fun. Any pictures of my friends drinking received a big thumbs up from me. I continued to convince myself that I wasn't addicted to alcohol for years, even though, deep down, I knew this wasn't true.

This internal conflict is called 'cognitive dissonance' and causes serious discomfort and anxiety, which is due to the lack of alignment between our desires and our beliefs. It's a form of internal hypocrisy, and no-one likes to think they're a hypocrite. This can lead us to seek justifications for our drinking; anything is better than living in a permanent state of mental noise and pain. This is why people who drink heavily, and who know the dangers, often carry on with it. They could quit drinking but that seems too much of a challenge, so they convince themselves that the messages they hear about the dangers of alcohol are not as bad as they sound. They might avoid reading anything in the media about the problems caused by alcohol, and instead focus more on the stories promoting the benefits. They may also compare themselves only to people who drink more than they do in order to make their habits seem moderate. By doing this they ease the internal conflict and convince themselves (falsely) that their behaviour is fine.

All this is a roundabout way of saying that rather than wondering if you're an alcoholic, you're far better off focusing your time and energy on making a positive change to your relationship with alcohol. Instead of wasting your time searching Google to convince yourself you're okay, gather the information you need to decide whether or not you should become someone who no longer drinks. As I mentioned before, I don't care for labels, I just don't drink now.

Another option is to ask yourself: 'Who holds the power in my life? Is it me or is it alcohol?' Be honest with yourself and make a list of the occasions on which you've put alcohol ahead of the important things, and reflect on your answers. Is this the way you want your life to be?

Here's my list of important things that I used to put alcohol ahead of.

My relationship with my daughter. I recall one occasion when she wanted to go to the cinema with me in the evening and I wanted to stay at home and drink. So she and my wife went to the cinema and I stayed home with me beloved wine. The alcohol won, and did for years.

My relationship with my wife. There were so many times when she wanted to go out and do something active and healthy, and I turned to drinking instead. I missed out on walks in nature, bike rides, and theme park visits, to name a few. I also knew my wife had concerns about how much I drank, so I hid the extent of my problem from her which meant I felt dishonest.

My friends. I neglected them and didn't invest time in creating new friendships, because I was more interested in drinking (either on my own or with others).

My work and career. Drinking every night impacted on my levels of focus, motivation, and productivity. I often felt like I was simply functioning my way through the day.

My health and wellbeing. I regularly had fears and worries about my health, and suspected it was only a matter of time before the amount I drank started to take its toll permanently.

Exercise and fitness. Hangovers combined with a lack of energy and motivation resulted in numerous skipped sessions at the gym.

In fact, I found that I was putting booze in front of just about everything in my life – it always came first and had the power. If you think you're doing the same, you need to keep reading this book.

Chapter 3
But I'm not like them

Have you ever looked at a homeless person drinking spirits from a bottle wrapped in a brown paper bag? I used to see someone like that and think to myself, 'Well I'm not as bad as him, so I must be okay.' This was a way of justifying my drinking and convincing myself I didn't really have a problem. Instead of feeling sorry for the guy, I used his misfortune to make myself feel better and to help calm the turbulence in my head.

How could I be as bad as them? I had a loving family, a lovely house, a nice car, my own business, and a few holidays to exotic destinations every year. Surely I was alright? Wrong… because *what I didn't have was freedom*. I was never truly happy or at peace, and rarely found myself feeling calm or laughing without a care. Life coach Tony Robbins says, 'Success without fulfilment is failure,' and for me, this seems true. I had all the material possessions I wanted, along with the love and support of my wonderful wife and family, but I didn't have true fulfilment. In fact, I felt like a failure.

The fact is, it doesn't matter whether you're a down-and-out drinking vodka in a park or whether you are able to function at work during the day after a heavy night of drinking. If alcohol holds power over you, and if you suspect you're trapped in a vicious cycle that you can't break out of, you're not free either. Because if you're simply going through the motions of your day until you can have the next drink, there's very little in the way of happiness on offer. Well, there wasn't for me anyway.

The most beautiful effect I experienced after a few weeks of not drinking was that I started to engage more with my wife and daughter. I was no longer putting wine first, and had the desire and energy to spend time with them. I loved listening to what they had to say, and found myself laughing as we shared jokes and played pranks on each other. When I looked back and wrote in my journal a list of the things that I'd neglected because of alcohol, I felt sad when I saw how I'd put wine ahead of quality time with my daughter, my wife, or my mum. However, writing this list also gave me strength as it made me realise what I should be putting first now – and it wasn't booze.

Take some time to jot down your own list of people, situations, and events that you've neglected in favour of drink. Then write next to each entry what the same situation or event would have looked like if you hadn't been drinking. You'll find this process eye-opening and empowering, even if it does make you feel down.

I now realise that just because I hadn't reached the point at which I was homeless and drinking on the streets, it didn't mean that I was any different to that guy. No doubt he'd encountered some bad luck in his life that meant things had worked out badly for him. But the fact is we're all caged in a self-built prison of booze, and we don't know how to get out.

The good news is that you hold the key to that prison, as we'll explore in the next chapter.

Chapter 4
The self-built prison to which you hold the key

I've often thought that the hardest part of quitting drinking is the period during which you're aware you have a problem but are unsure as to how you're going to solve it. This 'pain point' is fairly early in the journey and you can feel like you're trapped. Until you have a clear idea of how to make a change, it may seem as if half of you wants to quit and the other half wants to keep drinking to numb the thoughts, ease the pain, and blot everything out.

So even though in my drinking days, I was miserable, full of anxiety, unfulfilled, and suffering from many of the physical effects you would expect of a heavy drinker, I found that the more I wanted to stop, the more I drank. It was so frustrating because I couldn't see how to give it up. I even started buying wine boxes because it saved getting two or three bottles, and also meant that nobody could see how much I'd consumed.

I had created a prison for myself and couldn't see how to escape. But I eventually learned that I'd had the key to the lock all along and it was fairly simple to step forward, turn it, and break out of there.

So what was the key?

It was becoming curious, which led to a change in my mindset about alcohol. The book *This Naked Mind* and the free accompanying online programme, *The Alcohol Experiment*, enabled me to undo my beliefs and change my thinking. This programme is a free, interactive 30-day experiment with video tutorials, online journaling, and a structured approach to exploring your beliefs about alcohol and how you want it to feature in your life. Once you've read this book, if you still feel you need to make a change, then Annie's book and programme are great places to head to next.

It took me many years to commit to stopping drinking, even though the voices telling me to do so had been banging on in my head for so long. Of course, I wish I'd made the change 10 years ago, but I don't dwell on what might have been. I've accomplished it now and it's the best thing I've ever done. I like to look forward, not back.

The good news is that once you commit to making a change and come up with a strategy, everything gets much easier. This approach is the key to changing your mindset: be open-minded and curious. Just because you believe that, 'I can't go to a party without drinking, it won't be fun,' doesn't mean it's true. Try to get used to exploring your thoughts and feelings instead of just accepting them. Start to become inquisitive, be an internal detective, and pause for a moment when uncomfortable thoughts and feelings come to mind. Interrogate them – write them down and dig deep.

I want you to start looking at your beliefs around alcohol and challenging them, because I bet most of them are wrong. As a starting point, think of five types of events or situations which you believe are improved by alcohol, then make a second list detailing why and how they could be better *without* alcohol involved. Here are some examples of beliefs that people have posted in my Facebook group. By examining them and getting to the absolute truth of each statement, it's possible to unlock a 'new truth' that's more positive and powerful. I'll go into beliefs in more detail in a couple of chapters, but for now, I'd like you to consider these examples.

Current belief:
I can never say no to people when they want to go out drinking after work. I just get taken advantage of and say yes to boozing all the time.

Statement that's true after exploring the evidence around the original belief:
I have the power to say no if I choose to do so, and I plan to start being more mindful about what I say yes to.

Current belief:
I fail at everything I do – I doubt I can do this.

Statement that's true after exploring the evidence around the original belief:
If I don't try, I won't ever know. I'll approach this with an open mind and a sense of curiosity.

Current belief:
All my friends drink, so they probably won't want to know me if I quit alcohol.

Statement that's true after exploring the evidence around the original belief:
My true friends will be supportive and will look out for me.

Current belief:
I always have a drink in the evenings in front of the TV, so now what?

Statement that's true after exploring the evidence around the original belief:
There are hundreds of amazing, zero-alcohol drinks that could fill the void and I'm looking forward to trying them all.

Current belief:

I'm scared about telling people I've quit drinking.

Statement that's true after exploring the evidence around the original belief:
I'm going to make a plan for how and when I tell people. It might even be fun, and some could become inspired by what I'm doing.

Think about which version you prefer and whether the 'new truth' could be true for you, because understanding the importance of beliefs is the key to the door you're looking for. We'll explore them in more depth shortly.

Chapter 5
Do you have to hit rock bottom to make a change?

I speak to many people who have found themselves on the path to sobriety because of a 'rock bottom' moment in their lives caused by their drinking. This is a time or event when they've reached the lowest possible point, and life seems as if it can't get any worse. It usually involves some seriously regrettable behaviour, such as driving under the influence, cheating on (or losing) a partner, or another misdemeanour that the sober version of themselves would be absolutely mortified by.

This happens. I've witnessed people lose their spouses and children, and others who end up in jail and even hospital. These incidents can be life-changing, but we have to remember that they are not always so in a purely negative way (even though it seems like it at the time). This is because the rock bottom moment can bring with it a feeling of clarity and a clear vision that things need to change. After all, from the bottom, there is only one direction to travel and that's upwards.

I never had a rock bottom moment, although I had plenty of reasons to regret my behaviour. I simply reached a point at which I was sick and tired of the damage alcohol was causing, both internally and externally. You don't need to have had a rock bottom moment to discover you need to make a change; there are no rules of entry to the world of 'alcohol-free'. No matter where you are or what has gone before, the fact that you're reading this book is evidence that you're serious about making a lasting change. Give yourself a big pat on the back.

And does this mean that if you haven't had a rock bottom moment, you've got off lightly? Not really. As I say, I didn't have one but I can remember numerous episodes when I came close to it. Maybe if I'd crashed into the depths 10 years earlier, I might have made a change more quickly. Without it, I continued for years in blissful unawareness that I even had a problem, followed by more years of pain when I realised I did have one, but had no idea of how to solve it.

The most important thing to realise is that however you ended up here, reading this page, you're serious about taking back control in your life. Don't dwell on the past, but move forward, just like you will move forward through the pages in this book.

Chapter 6
The power of beliefs

Here are a few of my past beliefs:

That I needed to drink alcohol to have fun.
That I need alcohol to relax.
That alcohol eased my anxiety.

Now I know:

I have more fun without alcohol involved.
I'm more relaxed when I don't drink.
Alcohol is like fuel on the fire of anxiety – it makes it worse.

For almost three decades, I was convinced that the first set of statements were true and, of course, my behaviour reflected this – beliefs are powerful because they control our actions. However, the idea that what I believed could be *wrong* was foreign to me. This is what we humans are like – when we believe something, we think it's an absolute fact. However, contrary to popular opinion, beliefs are not always true. Who knew? I thought I was always right about everything!

Not only that, but beliefs live in our subconscious mind, affecting what we think is right and wrong without us realising it; they serve to make us the people we are. They're formed from the experiences we have throughout our lives and the information we digest, especially in childhood. When we were kids we didn't have the ability to tell the difference between truth and falsehood, so we believed without question what we were told which is where our core beliefs started to form. Of course, I still believe in Santa Claus – my mum and dad would never have lied to me.

So we don't get to choose what we believe, but when we become aware of it we can take back control. The way I found complete freedom from alcohol was by changing my beliefs about it. I mention this a lot and make no apology for it, as I hope the repetition will help make the message stick. When I changed my false belief that 'alcohol was serving me and improving my life' giving up started to feel fairly easy. I moved from a place of feeling deprived that I couldn't drink any longer to simply not wanting alcohol in my life again. Suddenly, I felt like I knew the real truth.

While this might sound simple, I can't just tell you to go and change your beliefs. If I could it would be really easy, but it's something you need to do for yourself. Become curious about your own beliefs and start to question how true they really are. Do this by writing down the reasons you think that alcohol makes your life better.

My answers would have been:

It makes me relax.
It eases my anxiety.
It makes me funny.
It helps me to have a good time.
It makes me forget the stresses of the day.

Then start to dig into your answers one by one and ask yourself how much truth the statements hold, and also if the opposite might be true.

My responses to the first three answers would have been:

It makes me relax
I've actually been at my most relaxed in situations when I haven't been drinking, and I know I've felt wonderfully at ease after a

longer period of no alcohol. I also feel more tense the day after drinking.

So now, this belief is not feeling quite so true – hopefully, you get the idea.

It eases my anxiety
It does so for a couple of hours, but it's always much worse the next day; then I drink again and the cycle of pain continues. I know from experience that when I have time away from alcohol my anxiety fades, so I don't believe that alcohol eases anxiety, it makes it worse.

It makes me funny
I might believe I'm funny when I've been drinking – alcohol is the master of illusion. But I know I've had numerous arguments and become aggressive and short-tempered with alcohol inside me. A few hours after I've drunk I also feel sluggish and low unless I have another drink. The next morning I don't feel motivated and often have headaches and a general lack of energy. None of this is funny.

While delving into your beliefs is a great way to question them and ask if they're true for you, another method of changing a belief is to experience the opposite of it for real out in the big wide world. In fact, there's no better way, because you then have cast-iron evidence of its falseness and it will naturally change to the new truth for you.

A great example would be this belief that I held for years: *'I can't have fun at a music gig without drinking.'* A few months after I quit, I attended my first gig without alcohol, and instead of racing to the bar as soon as I entered the arena to buy several pints of beer (so I didn't have to keep queuing), I watched the support band. I found it incredible that I'd made it all the way to the main act without needing to pee. I would have usually had at least three visits to the toilet by this time, and multiple more trips to the bar replenishing my beer supply.

When the band came on (Mumford & Sons – you may know them) I became immersed in the music and atmosphere, dancing without a care in the world. I had the time of my life, and the most awesome thing of all was that I got to drive home (no waiting for taxis in a huge queue in the rain) and climb into my comfy bed, before waking up (hangover free) with vivid memories of the night before. Not to mention the joy that there was no regrettable behaviour or being sick to be ashamed of the next morning.

The long-held belief that I had to drink to have fun at a gig had been well and truly destroyed; I now knew differently because I'd experienced it for real. It even made me start thinking about all the other gigs I'd been to in the past, and I regretted being so blind drunk that I hadn't enjoyed them like the Mumford & Sons one. This was how I wanted all gigs to be from now on.

If you haven't done so already, take the time to write down all of your beliefs about alcohol. Be totally honest and open with yourself, and dig into whether the statements you made are true. You need to be like a detective looking for evidence to prove or disprove the statements, and once you've gathered all the information together you can ask yourself whether the original belief still holds true or not.

For me, I found that challenging my beliefs was the biggest game-changer on the journey to complete freedom from alcohol. Once they'd shifted, I simply realised that I had no desire to drink, and I was motivated to start sharing the message about the dangers of alcohol and the ease with which you could cut it out of your life if you really wanted to.

To start changing your beliefs, I recommend you continue reading this book, and also work your way through the steps below so you can analyse them in more depth. Here are a few examples of beliefs that you might firmly believe to be true:

Without drinking each day I'll never be happy.
Drinking enables me to feel confident in myself.
Alcohol lowers my inhibitions and enables me to meet new people –
I could never do this without drinking.

I'd like you to look at your own list of beliefs and follow the same process as I have detailed below. Try and assign feelings to each one, because it's the *emotions* that sit at the root of the pain and misery caused by the beliefs. As an example, I recently went to a wedding and believed it was acceptable not to wear a tie as I'd heard it was a fairly informal affair. The belief itself caused me no pain – there was no reason for it to. But when I arrived at the wedding and saw all the guys with formal suits and ties, I suddenly felt negative emotions. I thought that people were judging me and I felt embarrassed. It wasn't the belief that upset me, it was the feeling of self-consciousness that went with it.

So let's assign some emotions (or feelings) to my examples above:

Without drinking each day, I'll never be happy – worry, sadness.
Drinking enables me to feel confident in myself – self-judgement, shame.
Alcohol lowers my inhibitions and enables me to meet new people –
I could never do this without drinking – shyness, unhappiness.

These are just examples; you can make your list as long as you wish and add as many emotions as you like. Once you have written it, you need to recognise that these beliefs are false truths; you need to replace the old beliefs with new and truthful ones, and back them up with evidence so you know they represent the real truth for you. Also, rather than writing 'I can't' or 'I won't', try to use statements such as 'I feel' or 'I can'.

Let's look at how I might express myself using my examples with a new truth.

The statement:

Without drinking each day I'll never be happy.

Could become:

I am happy (give yourself some reasons why, with examples), but I have a hard time not drinking every day. So I'm working on this to become stronger.

The statement:

Drinking enables me to feel confident in myself.

Could become:

I can be confident (give yourself some reasons why and examples), but I use alcohol as false armour and I'm working on changing this and experiencing life without it.

The statement:

Alcohol lowers my inhibitions and enables me to meet new people – I could never do this without drinking.

Could become:

I can meet new people (give yourself some reasons why, with examples) – I feel like alcohol makes it easier but I'm working on this so that I can grow as a person.

Now look back over your statements and say them out loud to yourself. Which one feels like the truth for you now? Which one feels better? Which one do you want to stick with? Look at your 'new truths' and take some time to reflect on them. Keep working on your beliefs, and if one comes up that's creating negative emotions, it's time to bring it out into the light so that you can create a new and more positive version. Use this strategy to work through the situation whenever this happens.

I hope that the information I've shared in this part of this book will have already enabled you to start challenging many of your beliefs about alcohol and how it might be serving you. This strategy will enable you to become mindful about your beliefs, so you can start catching yourself in the act of believing false statements about alcohol, and ask yourself 'why' when you experience negative emotions.

Chapter 7
Your all-or-nothing mentality

'All or nothing': that describes me perfectly. Are you a bit like that or do you know someone who is, who can't do anything by halves?

Everything I do in my life, I have to commit to it, heart, mind, body, and soul; otherwise, I feel like it isn't worth bothering with at all. This means I sometimes start projects and don't finish them because I get stuck in and then think I can't do it perfectly, so I give up. Or I simply become bored because events aren't moving quickly enough for my impatient brain. There's no evidence that what's often called an addictive personality exists, but I know from personal experience that, once I throw myself into something, I have a rush of pleasure endorphins and want to experience more and more of it.

A great example of my all-or-nothing mentality is my running. Around six years ago, I took it up and before long completed my first 5k race, followed swiftly by a 10k. Did I stop there? No. I've since run 15 marathons and one ultra-marathon. (I also ran almost every one of those marathons having drunk wine 'to calm my nerves' the night before, followed by drinking afterwards to 'celebrate my success'.)

I'm also highly impulsive, and find this same trait among many others who are questioning whether alcohol is serving them well. There's nothing wrong with this, but over the years I've learned to recognise the times when I need to pause and reflect before I jump into something with both feet. I still find it a challenge at times, and recently ended up buying an expensive sports car within an hour of wandering past the showroom!

Over time, I've worked out that being an all-or-nothing person is a bit like having a superpower. It's enabled me to manage far more than I set out to achieve with various projects – everything from writing this book, growing my own successful business, completing marathons, and speaking and coaching about alcohol. All good stuff... However, what I've also learned is that when you mix an all-or-nothing personality with a highly addictive substance, it's a dangerous combination that doesn't usually end well.

Now, this may not apply to you – you may not be an all-or-nothing person. But I've found a high percentage of heavy drinkers fall into this category, so if you recognise yourself here I highly recommend digging into your relationship with alcohol and taking steps to make a positive change. Alcohol is like kryptonite (the crystal from the planet Krypton that eliminates Superman's powers) to all-or-nothing people – it takes away your strength and effectiveness.

The good news is that when you channel your all-or-nothing mentality into positive activities, the outcomes are often amazing. It really is a gift, but you need to use it wisely and keep it away from addictive substances. This is what I did when I channelled my impulsiveness into creating the sober life I wanted and deserved. I even became a little addicted to sobriety.

In fact, the most significant shift in my life has come from moving my all-or-nothing behaviour from destructiveness to constructiveness. When I was drinking and something went wrong at work or in my personal life, I would throw my toys out of the pram in an instant. But since I cut alcohol out of my life, my brain has recalibrated and I'm much more rational and level-headed. Things just don't get to me as much now, and I have more mental resilience. For instance, my teenage daughter recently had some tough times with love and relationships. The old drinking me would have been useless and far more interested in having another glass of wine than listening and helping. I would have likely ended up being argumentative and unsupportive, and probably made the situation worse. But the alcohol-free me is a different person. I reached out to her and we spoke like grown-ups, working through the problems; together we solved it and dad received a big hug at the end.

Likewise, within my work – running a marketing company – I used to have a meltdown if we had issues with staff or complaints from clients. If someone left us a bad review online it was a huge trigger, and I would assume it meant the end of the business. Not long ago, I had the chance to put my newfound resilience to the test when someone was kind enough to leave us a one-star review. I was actually happy about it because it gave me the opportunity to test how I would react, and to my pleasure, I felt calm. I took the time to look at the feedback the client had left, investigate the complaint, call him up, and have a professional discussion about what we could do to address his concerns. At the end of the call, the guy was so happy he signed up for a further six months and removed the review.

On that first day of quitting drinking, when I was full of fear and worry, I wish I'd known about all the wonderful and amazing gifts that were waiting for me in a life without alcohol. I needn't have worried at all. I would've been like a child on Christmas Eve, excited to unwrap my presents; but unlike Christmas, which is over in a day, sobriety just keeps giving more and more gifts. It's just a shame we don't get to unwrap them on day one when we're looking longingly at the unopened bottle of wine.

All this from putting down the bottle – it's incredible and so unexpected. Annie Grace talks about the 'Big Domino' in your life – this is the one thing that when you push it over, causes everything else to change. For me, that domino was alcohol, but I never expected so much else to shift. Have you ever thought about what the big domino is in your life?

Chapter 8
Why drinking in moderation doesn't work

When we start questioning our relationship with alcohol, the thought of quitting drink forever seems overwhelming. It's natural to look for some kind of compromise as a way of calming the turmoil in our brains, and we think, 'Maybe I can just cut down without giving up altogether.'

When I realised I no longer had power over alcohol, cutting down was my first thought too. I decided I would be disciplined, change my habits, and just have a couple of glasses each night, Monday to Thursday; then, at the weekend, I'd drink my usual bottle or more of red. I decided this strategy would significantly reduce the number of alcohol units I was having and make me feel better about my habit (although the truth was I was still quaffing 90 plus units a week, even with my moderation plan in place).

The final tactic I tried was watering the red wine down; this way, I figured I could have the same number of glasses each evening but would be consuming less alcohol. I started by adding one-third water to two-thirds red wine and, over the coming days, increased it until after a few weeks it was two-thirds water and one-third wine. This worked for a while, but before long, I found myself craving a glass of the strong stuff until I gave in and poured myself one.

From both my own personal journey and the experiences of thousands of people I've helped, I can tell you right now:

moderation hardly ever works. People who can moderate their drinking and stay in control generally don't buy books about sobriety. If you could drink like those 'normal' people, would you be reading this? Accepting that you don't have power over alcohol is a significant step towards claiming it back.

Generally, we 'enthusiastic drinkers' can't do things by halves – that's why we have this addiction in the first place. As I mentioned previously, we're often all-or-nothing kind of people and one glass is never enough. This meant that I found moderating my drinking to be a huge internal struggle. All I was thinking about on the 'drink less' days was the fact that I couldn't have my usual amount of wine; I'd feel miserable all day and evening because I wasn't having my habitual fill of the red stuff. I felt deprived.

Moderation requires willpower and willpower works like a muscle – over time it tires and eventually gives out. I learned the hard way that my resolve wasn't strong enough to keep reducing my drinking, and I decided to cut it out altogether. That way I broke free from the booze by making **ONE** decision to stop forever. I looked at it as if I was ending a troubled relationship that it was time to break up from, so alcohol and I got divorced. I even wrote a divorce letter to wine which gave me a real sense of closure; you can read it on the *Be Sober* blog. When you feel ready to break up, I highly recommend that you write your own letter too.

By making **ONE** decision it meant that I never had to make any other decisions, and could get on with my life. There was no longer a daily struggle as to whether I should drink that night or not, or if I was going to drink, worrying about how much I should (or shouldn't) have. The decision was made, it was over, and that was the end of it. Simple.

If you're reading this and worrying about your drinking, by all means, try cutting down and if it works for you, that's great. But I strongly suspect the long-term solution will be quitting totally and walking away from that bad relationship forever.

Chapter 9
The power of journaling

When I finally made it past day one of not drinking (after many failed attempts), I decided I should keep a diary of my feelings and experiences so that I could look back on it one day and see how far I'd come. Annie Grace's *The Alcohol Experiment* online programme includes the facility to journal online each day, and this was perfect for me as I'm not a fan of pen and paper, so I decided to put my thoughts and feelings down in my account there. Working through the programme also gave me a structure for what to write, as it offered daily topics to explore and journal about.

If you haven't checked it out yet do take a look by visiting www.thealcoholexperiment.com. It holds your hand through the first 30 days of exploring the role that alcohol plays in your life. You'll be presented with all the facts about drinking, and you are empowered to question your beliefs to see if they're true for you. You're under no pressure to do anything more than treat it as an experiment; you can then make a decision about how you want to live (or not) with alcohol as you approach the 30th day of the programme.

After a week or two of updating my online journal, I decided I would prefer to write more in-depth pieces about my sober journey so I started the *Be Sober* blog. You can find the blog by visiting www.besober.co.uk – I've updated it regularly ever since and shared many personal stories, as well as tips and advice. I found writing to be an amazing tool that helped me through those early weeks and months of sobriety, and it became an outlet that drinking used to fill. I only started the blog to help myself, but as the weeks and months went by, I started to see the visitor numbers growing. People were leaving comments saying that my posts had helped them, and they also thanked me for being open, honest and sharing.

Keeping a journal isn't for everyone so you need to make your own decision about whether it's right for you. But I think it genuinely helps, and I now blog about my progress as often as I can. Your journal will also help you to learn from your experiences and grow stronger; it's a powerful tool when it comes to giving you support, inspiration and motivation. Recording your feelings is a way of understanding them, and the outpouring onto paper can help your mental and physical wellbeing. The very process of writing has also been shown to improve your immune system, lower blood pressure, and increase the function of your lungs and liver.

You don't have to do it online – an old-fashioned book journal works just as well if you prefer. I strongly recommend you keep one for at least the first year as you explore your relationship with drinking. Some people I know have gone so far as to say that their journal was their biggest support tool on the path to freedom from alcohol. Another great use for your journal is that it allows you to become strategic in your alcohol-free life. If you have an event coming up, you can put together your plan and your goals in writing ahead of time to ensure that you're set for success when the big day arrives.

Looking back over my journal and blog entries, it puts a smile on my face to see how far I've come. From drinking at least a bottle of wine every day for well over 20 years to becoming a sober coach, speaker and writer. Who would have thought that would ever happen? And my journal tells me how I did it, day by day.

Part Two
The problems and challenges you'll face

There are many books that help you when you want to quit drinking, but I've never been able to find one that serves as an ongoing support tool for the alcohol-free life ahead of you. That's why I wrote *The Sober Survival Guide*, to be your friend as you travel the path to complete freedom from alcohol. In a way, Part Two of this book is the advice I wish I'd had myself.

Even if you've managed to put alcohol out of your life, there will be days when you feel as if you can't do without it. Going to your first sober wedding or holiday are key examples, but sometimes you'll just think, 'I can't carry on.' This happens to all of us, so don't worry – my goal here is to give you the support you need to deal with whatever comes up.

I've spent well over a year researching the most common issues that arise, and in the following chapters, I address them in turn. Each is based on a specific problem, so I suggest you dip in and out of this part of the book as you need it. For this reason, there is some repetition across a few of the chapters, as I'm keen to make sure all the relevant information is there for you wherever you're looking for it; that's not a problem as it often takes a few tries for a message to sink in. It's also a good idea to keep the book handy, as it's your go-to emergency guide whenever you find life without drinking to be a struggle.

As well as speaking from my own experience, I've drawn on the testimonies of the thousands of people I've helped on their own journeys through both my coaching and my online group. What's more, to give you different perspectives and to reinforce the fact that you're in good company, you'll see that at various points I share quotes and comments from my *Be Sober* Facebook group. Thousands of other people are asking the same questions and facing the same challenges as you.

Sober Facebook groups are usually private groups, meaning nobody other than your group co-members can see what you post. This allows you to reach out to the community with confidentiality and confidence. Asking questions in these groups can give you fast feedback on your specific question or issue, and you'll receive a range of responses from a diverse mix of people at different stages of sobriety. Groups are also a great place to meet new friends who you have something in common with.

With all of that said, nothing in this book is intended to be a substitute for medical advice, and if you have any cause for concern around withdrawal symptoms, your health in general, or your mental well-being after you've quit drinking, please visit your doctor.

Chapter 10
I can't move past 'day (or week) one'

'I can't go even one day without drinking; quitting alcohol fills me with a sense of dread.'

When I made the decision to stop drinking alcohol, it took me quite a few attempts to get through 'day one' (or even 'week one') without wine. To be honest, I don't think there are many people who succeed at their first attempt and I was certainly no exception. Here I was, aged 44, having drunk red wine pretty much every night for over twenty years, so it's natural that I'd predict that quitting was going be a punishing struggle.

I still remember when I'd made it through my first day without drinking and it was the early evening of day two. My wife and I went for a run (one of my favourite hobbies) and while we were out, I was full of internal conflict. I couldn't focus on what I was doing because of the huge, swirling mass of mixed messages about red wine in my head. Half of my brain was saying that I 'couldn't' have a drink tonight because it was day two of my new sober life and I was working to be alcohol-free. Yet the other half was screaming that I deserved one because I'd had a stressful day at work and I didn't drink yesterday, so I had every reason to reward myself today. I started talking to my wife about how I was feeling and before I knew it, I had juddered to a halt on the street as tears poured down my face, with her hugging me like a child who'd fallen off his bike.

Well, I did drink that night, but I continued to work towards a life of freedom. After a few more failed attempts and a little more time, I was able to cut alcohol out of my life forever and not look back. I did it: I stopped. I didn't drink that final night and never, ever drank again (and never will). The reason I unlocked the door to true freedom was because I had changed my mindset. I was no longer thinking that I *couldn't have* wine, but that I *didn't want* it. I also went into my new sober life with a sense of excitement about what was ahead of me, rather than feeling deprived because I'd lost something. This involved reframing my thinking: what treats did I have to come? I couldn't wait to find out.

Annie Grace says that 'your expectations shape your experience' and this is so true. If you approach sobriety with a sense of loss, and tell yourself it's going to be hard, or you aren't going to have fun any longer, that's probably what will happen. You have the power to shape your experience, so you should be mindful of negative and unhelpful self-talk. Try and catch yourself when you do it and recast your assumption to new positive statements that are still true for you (see Chapter 23 for more on this).

When I started out, I had to go through a process of undoing my beliefs because I'd relied on wine to unwind at the end of every single day for so long. In my mind, alcohol was the elixir of happiness, so I wrote down all the things I loved about wine, each of which I believed to be totally true.

Some of my beliefs about red wine were:

- it made me relax;
- it eased my anxiety and worries;
- it made things more fun (I was hilarious and super-witty with wine inside me, right?), and
- it tasted good.

After several weeks sober, I looked back at that same list and started to dig deep into the statements, like a detective in a search of the truth. I approached them with an open mind and was totally honest in my answers. Below are the responses I wrote when I reflected back on my original statements:

It made me relax

I thought it made me relax, but in reality, it only enabled me to forget what was on my mind until the following day. What's more, I could become quite aggressive and unreasonable after I had a drink. The truth is that alcohol didn't make me relax, it only made me an arrogant arsehole. I remember seeing a video of myself after I'd been drinking and feeling embarrassed about the way I was behaving and talking to people.

It eased my anxiety and worries

All alcohol does is take away what it gave you, and then pay it forward. What I mean by this is that it may feel like your pain has been eased during the time you're drinking, but the next morning your problems and anxieties are still unresolved. Nothing has gone away just because you had a drink. After a night of boozing, I would wake up with my anxiety feeling worse than the day before; my worries were still there, but now in blindingly high definition. Over time, quitting alcohol caused the dark clouds of anxiety and worry to drift away and never come back. The sun came out, and I'm now happy to have it shining on me for the first time in a long time.

It made things more fun

Having a long period of not drinking to look back on now, I can see that if an event is fun, it's fun, regardless of alcohol. If you attend a rubbish, boring function, it's still rubbish and boring whether you have alcohol or not. Likewise, a fun night out with great friends is entertaining (even more so) without alcohol. Alcohol does not make anything more fun.

It tasted good

Can you remember how you reacted the first time you tasted an alcoholic drink, especially a neat spirit like vodka or whisky? I wouldn't mind betting you didn't compliment the wonderful taste or the smell of it! When I first tried drinking as a teenager it almost made me sick, but I pretended I liked it and eventually became used to it. That's because when we first try it our bodies send us a message that 'this stuff is bad'. They don't want it, but after we experience the first rush of endorphins our brains take over and we start to crave the same hit again. That's why I kept persevering and ended up being hooked on the addictive substance contained within the drink (which is what it's designed to do).

So what's the key to alcohol freedom? It's to delve into your beliefs and reach a place where you can change your mindset, so that alcohol becomes small and insignificant in your life. Once this change happened in my mind, I knew I was ready to successfully get through my first day without drinking and stick with it long-term. It felt so different once my beliefs and assumptions had shifted, and I found myself feeling excited about getting stuck into my new sober life.

However, I'm not going to sugar-coat it for you: the first days and weeks can be challenging. You're going through a huge life change, but with all the support groups, sober books and wonderful alcohol-free drinks around, you can turn it from being a hardship into something to embrace. I now consider myself 'passionately sober'. It isn't a chore and I'm not deprived; I love my new life, and I love that I am happy again – I can't remember feeling this at peace since I was a child. I just wish I'd kicked the booze sooner, but I look forward instead of backwards.

This is great, but what practical advice can you give?

If you're struggling to move past your first few days without alcohol, here are five actions you can take:

1. Arm yourself with some good sober books. *This Naked Mind* is the best in my opinion, but also check out *Alcohol Explained* by William Porter and *The Sober Diaries* by Clare Pooley.

2. Join some sober groups on Facebook. These are online communities filled with people at different stages of their journeys. You can share your experiences and receive advice and support from the other members, and they're also a great place to meet new people. I've found them to be an amazing support tool and have come across so many inspirational, caring, and supportive people through this kind of network. You can join the free, private *Be Sober* group by following the link on the website: www.besober.co.uk.

3. Join the 30-day *Alcohol Experiment* at www.thealcoholexperiment.com by Annie Grace. This is an excellent and free programme with daily videos that are structured to take you on a path of discovery about your relationship with alcohol. It enables you to start bringing your beliefs into the light, and to question whether they're actually true.

4. Arm yourself with plenty of alcohol-free drinks and have fun trying them out. This has been one of the most fun parts of sobriety for me, because there are so many amazing and wonderful grown-up drinks that don't contain alcohol. There's a whole new world of flavours waiting to be discovered, so go forward and enjoy it.

5. Have fun, get excited and enjoy the journey! There really is nothing to fear. Although it may feel like you're losing something from your life, the truth is you're gaining a lot more. Being sober is a gift that never stops giving; even though it may not feel like it at the start, it's the truth.

'Many of us here in the group are back at 'day one' and I've been thinking about this. Obviously, I had a million relapses before I

managed to quit so I sympathise. I think it's really important to pinpoint the exact minute you decided to drink. There was a point yesterday when you weren't drinking, then a minute later that changed. You had to go through all the steps: making the decision, getting the alcohol, opening it, finding a glass, pouring it, picking it up, and drinking it. Lots and lots went into that simple decision. You could have stopped at any point. So I wonder why we don't? For me, when I decided to drink, wildfire couldn't have stopped me. I would manipulate everyone or rage at anything in my way. I didn't even see it as a 'relapse' – it was simply me changing my mind about drinking and everyone else could go f**k themselves.

This only changes when you stop wanting to drink – when you stop associating it with reward and pleasure. It isn't easy to disassociate – after all, we were fed a lifetime of misleading information that alcohol would enhance our lives! Once we accept that alcohol holds no appeal – that it's a poisonous substance – then we can move on and fill our lives with other stuff.

The good news for anyone who has relapsed this weekend is that you've been sober before. You've already had days or weeks sober. So you know you can do it. Try and remember the moment you changed your mind, go back in time and think about exactly what your trigger was. Remember HALT – never get too hungry, angry, lonely (bored) or tired. Cravings are awful and powerful, but they do pass. Even something as simple as drinking a pint of water can stop them.

Good luck everyone this week – we all fall down but it's getting back up that counts.'
Be Sober Facebook group post by KL, Scotland

Chapter 11
I can't fill the void

'I need to have a glass in my hand; without it, I feel lost.'

When you're no longer drinking you'll find you have more time on your hands – it's a natural consequence of being sober. Combine this with raised levels of energy and a hunger to do more, and you have a recipe for true success and happiness. When I quit drinking I couldn't believe how much more capacity I had to get out and do things.

Once you've cut alcohol out of your life your brain and body will recalibrate and this can take a bit of time. Many people experience a feeling of happiness after a few weeks without drinking; this is called the 'pink cloud' phase and feels almost euphoric. When this happened to me I couldn't believe I was smiling and laughing naturally for the first time in over two decades. (Just a word of warning: keep your guard up because you can have the odd overcast day in the midst of the pink clouds – Chapter 21 covers this in more detail).

However, once you've moved past this delightful phase you can find the absence of booze leaves a void. For instance, my routine had been to drink red wine in front of the television every evening after my daughter had gone to bed, and after I quit, I still wanted to watch my box sets accompanied by an 'adult' drink in a grown-up glass. After considering the options and doing some research, I found there was a huge selection of new and exciting adult drinks for me to explore and taste.

I don't like to call these drinks 'alcohol-free' because they're not pretending to be an alcoholic drink; rather, they're botanical drinks that you can mix with tonic water (my favourite) or a mixer of your choice. I also love to add a slice of lime and ice. Some of the ones I've tried and loved are: Seedlip, Caleno, Ceders, Borrago, and Silk Tree. I update my blog with the latest drinks, so if you're keen to explore this tasty new world you can read my reviews.

You may also like to check out alcohol-free beers and wines, some of which are amazing. However, for some people they can act as a trigger so please do what feels right for you. I found alcohol-free red wine was not for me as it just seemed too much like the real thing.

Using these botanical drinks as a simple way of replacing alcoholic drinks has worked incredibly well for me and for many members of the *Be Sober* group. It may work for you too, because you feel like you're drinking something special; in fact, most of the people I speak to don't even notice the fact that the drink isn't alcoholic.

So although this is how I filled the void in my evening routine, quitting drinking also meant I had a lot more time on my hands and another gap to fill. After all, I used to spend several hours drinking every day, so when I added up that time over a month it was a lot of empty hours I was faced with. With all my new energy and motivation pulsing through me, I filled the gap by getting out into the big wide world to explore hobbies. This meant I was able to spend time on the things I truly enjoyed; I even started drawing and writing again, which I hadn't done for years.

One of my initiatives was to join a fitness boot-camp, where I made loads of new friends (those friendships are so much more authentic when they aren't built on a foundation of drinking). I started going to a Pilates class, and spent more time running, walking in the woods, reading books, and going to gigs and sporting events. I also watched just about every film that came out at the cinema.

How did I start? It was my old friend 'writing things down' again. I made a list in my journal of all the activities I wanted to do, from the simple through to the crazy ones that I may never get around to (white water rafting just seems too dangerous). If making a list seems like a good idea to you, go ahead and get your journal and pen it out. I even stuck a list of mine on the fridge and have been ticking off the things I've accomplished.

The point is, do what you enjoy with the extra energy you've released. Don't sit around getting bored or wasting time thinking about drinking – step out and love it. Take the time to think about the activities you'd like to do now you have more time and energy; use your hunger to participate in the world and get stuck in.

If you need some ideas about what to do, there are hundreds of activities you can get involved in. Below are a few suggestions:

- plan a trip to upcoming concerts, gigs and shows;
- learn an instrument;
- learn to speak a language;
- explore art and crafts-based hobbies;
- join a fitness group;
- join a yoga or Pilates class;
- take up swimming;
- take up cooking classes;
- spend time walking or cycling in the great outdoors, or
- volunteer with a local group or charity and start helping people.

'60 days alcohol-free! Feeling great these days and I've learned a lot, been indulging in some new hobbies and used the money I would have spent on alcohol to instead have a week away in Denmark. And the best part is, I've barely thought about drinking at all! I think this new lease of life is my new addiction now.'
Facebook group post by Matt

Chapter 12
I'm terrified of 'coming out'

'How do I tell people I don't drink? This scares me.'

After a couple of weeks of being sober and realising that I would never return to drinking alcohol again, I was feeling rather proud of myself and wanting to tell people. However, I had read in some sober books that not everyone might be as excited and enthusiastic as I was. So I started by breaking the news to family members. I told them what I'd been drinking (buckets of red wine every night), and that I felt it had been taking over my life and had stopped me from being happy. They were really supportive and helped me to talk openly about my drinking; they even continued to check on my progress as the months went by.

I also had a lovely chat with my teenage daughter, and was careful to avoid being preachy or pushing my new-found views on her. I gave her all the facts and decided I would let my actions do the talking, so she could hopefully learn from them.

After this, I told a few close friends, but these conversations didn't necessarily go quite so well. One of my mates insisted on telling me that it was 'just a phase', and surely I could have 'just one drink' when I went out with him. I made it crystal clear that I wouldn't ever be drinking again, and re-explained how much I'd been drinking and why I had to stop. It would never be 'just one drink'. 'One drink' to me would mean returning to a lifetime of alcohol addiction again – no thanks! Unfortunately, this didn't make a difference, and he spent the next couple of weeks posting pictures on Facebook of nights we'd been out drinking together along with comments about how wonderful it had been. Thanks for being so supportive!

At this point, I decided it was him who had the problem, not me. I knew he had his own issues with drink and I think his adverse reaction was probably because he had concerns about his own alcohol intake. He might also have felt like he'd lost a drinking buddy, and I was sorry for that, but nothing was going to change my mind about becoming sober. I've since looked more closely at the way in which some people react, and have realised that it can make them feel judged when a friend says they've quit drinking, as well as force them to hold a mirror up to their own relationship with alcohol. This can be uncomfortable and it is why announcing you have cut alcohol out of your life can attract the occasional unwanted comment.

After a month or so I decided it was time to 'come out' fully, and wrote a post on my personal Facebook page stating that quitting drinking was the best thing I'd ever done and that it had made me feel happier than at any time I could remember. This was met with a mixture of comments along the lines of, 'You're getting old and boring,' although there were a few that congratulated me with, 'Well done mate, I could never do that.'

I guess the issue is that most drinkers just don't get it, because a love of alcohol has been ingrained into all of us since childhood. We sober warriors have committed the ultimate act of rebellion by turning our backs on what almost everyone else thinks is the only way to behave. I suppose it's inevitable that a lot of people will question our new life choice and react negatively to it. 'Why would you do that?' is another reaction I've heard a few times. Someone else wrote a comment to me: 'It won't last.' When I first read it, it was like a red rag to a bull (not that I needed any more motivation, but it certainly helped). I like to look back on it from time to time, and even keep a screenshot of it on my phone.

The thing is, I was so excited about quitting drinking. Sobriety was delivering more and more wonderful gifts to me, and I wanted to tell anyone who would listen. In hindsight, I should probably have taken the time to craft a strategy for how and when to tell people, rather than plastering it all over social media without much thought. I think some of my friends thought I'd become a crazy sober preacher, so these days I only tend to raise the topic if someone instigates the conversation.

So what's the best way to tell people you don't drink alcohol?

The good news is that you hold the power; it's totally up to you, so do whatever you feel is right and at a time that's good for you. There's no rush or deadline – some people take years to tell other people about their relationship with alcohol. If you're using a journal it's well worth writing down who you're going to tell, when you're going to tell them, and how you plan on doing it.

It's also worth having a strategy for when you're out and about, as you don't want to be caught off guard if someone questions your drinking (or lack of it). If I'm going to an event, I like to visualise the whole thing before I go. Everything from what I'm wearing, to parking the car, through to going inside and meeting people. I think about how the conversations will go and how the evening will look; I picture every detail and play it through until it's time to leave and head home. I find this to be a helpful way of getting mentally set for success, and to be ready when I'm asked what I would like to drink or why I'm not drinking alcohol.

If I'm offered a drink I usually just say, 'No thanks, I don't drink.' This often prompts further questions, but in those cases, I take an honest approach. The same applies with closer friends – I simply tell them, 'I no longer drink because I was drinking far too much red wine and it was impacting on my quality of life.' If they want to discuss it further, I'm happy to tell them more. I could easily make an excuse like, 'I'm driving tonight' or 'I'm on medication,' but I prefer to be true to myself. I've found the honest approach has also enabled many people to open up to me about their own drinking.

So when you consider what you plan to say and whether you should be honest or use an excuse, bear in mind that if you tell the truth you may give someone a beacon of hope. When you quit drinking you'll inspire other people, whether you like it or not. It's my opinion that if we make excuses, we can deprive people of the opportunity to open up. There are thousands of drinkers who know they have a problem but don't know what to do about it, so when you bring up this rather uncomfortable topic and start talking openly about it, they can see hope and inspiration. Obviously, it's up to you and you need to do what feels right, but do think about this when you make your decision.

'Talk about accountability... I just came out on Facebook. How funny that's actually a thing to "come out" that you don't drink anymore.'
Be Sober Facebook Group Post by CS, Gainesville, VA, USA

I've listed below a few lines you could use if you're attending a social function. Have a think about what will work for you, try out a few, and maybe make your own list.

'I don't drink. I used to but I couldn't control it.' This is you being totally honest, but you may not feel comfortable confessing to people that you couldn't control alcohol. The sure thing about this one, though, is that nobody will push you to have another drink, and I almost guarantee that people will start opening up to you about their own drinking.
'I don't drink, I don't like the taste of it.'
'I don't drink, it doesn't agree with me.'
'I can't drink, I'm driving.'
'I'm on medication, I can't drink.'
'I don't drink, I've already drunk my lifetime's quota.'
'I avoid alcohol for personal reasons.'
'Not now, thanks.'
'No thanks, I don't like how alcohol makes me feel.'

'I'm training for a marathon (or another event) and I'm not drinking while I'm training.'
'I'm doing an alcohol-free challenge this month.'
'I'm allergic to alcohol.'
'I don't like myself when I drink.'
'Not tonight, maybe another time.'
'I'm pregnant.' (Obviously, only try this if you're a woman.)
'No thanks, I'm annoying enough when I am sober.'
'Alcohol gives me awful headaches.'
'Yes, I'd love a drink, can I have an orange juice please.'
'No thanks, I'm a nightmare when I'm drunk and you don't want to see that.'

These are just a few examples out of hundreds of possible lines you could use. Keep your guard up for the odd strange reaction, and always remember if it happens, it's not you, it's them. In fact, it's not even them, it's the alcohol and their relationship with it that makes them respond negatively.

On the sober journey you may well find that your relationships with some of your friends change, especially if, like mine, many of them were based purely around alcohol. Sadly, this can be one of the sacrifices that comes with an alcohol-free life, although you might find yourself questioning if they were true friends in the first place. True friends will be supportive and will never judge you or try and stop you doing what you feel is right. The good news is that I've made some incredible new friends since I quit drinking, and these friendships are some of the most genuine I've ever experienced.

'I feel like a fraud! I have 'come out' as a non-drinker to almost everyone in my life. My family, friends, and most importantly, Facebook. I have made myself publicly accountable and I have found it really helpful. Bizarrely, at work, I just can't do it. There is a heavy drinking culture at my work, and I used to be part of it. Constant jokes about 'wine o'clock' and 'is there gin in that mug'. They constantly talk about hungover-Mondays and can't-wait-for-

Fridays. So what is weird is that I still join in. They joke about heavy weekends and I smile and agree. They say 'you'll need a gin tonight' and I say 'or two!'

It is so strange. All I could say to the one colleague I am closest to was, 'I've cut right down – can't be bothered anymore.' She laughed and said, 'Yeah right, to just a few bottles a day.' I laughed too.

I wonder why I continue to pretend? I'm 46, I can't be trying to be cool, can I? Why do they even think drinking is cool? I guess I just don't want to lose all the water cooler moments – I want to be fun and join in the banter and I don't want to be left out. All the reasons people are afraid to stop drinking.

I thought my lying days were over when I quit. I used to lie like a rug! Always hiding my bottles, lying about when I last drank or how much. Even when I did alcohol-free days every week, I always faked a couple.

Is anyone else still lying to people in their lives?'
Facebook group post by KL, Scotland

Chapter 13
I've slipped up

'I've had a drink after I quit and feel like a failure.'

It's important to understand that almost everyone slips up – it's part of the journey. I've been where you are now, feeling like a failure after promising myself (and my wife) over and over again that I was going to stop, only to find myself finishing off a bottle of red wine later that evening. It took me so many attempts to even move past day one; after all, I'd drunk every day for twenty-plus years. Believe me when I say that if I managed to find freedom, you can too.

It can be easy to allow negative self-talk to creep in and to start calling yourself a failure after trying to quit alcohol for the hundredth time and still having a drink. My advice is to take a step back and a deep breath (as well as reading Chapter 23 about negative self-talk). Gaining long-term sobriety is a bit like a toddler learning to walk for the first time: we're all new on this journey and need to learn from our mistakes. So to start with we walk a little and then we fall flat on our faces – ouch! Next time, we walk further but when we fall, we know to put our hands out to avoid smashing our face. From here we start to understand how to stay balanced and walk longer distances, and before we know it, we're taking bolder steps and rarely falling down. With more practice and growing confidence, we're able to walk for miles without toppling over. Nobody ever learned to walk without trial and error, and we all master it in the end.

First of all, you're not a failure. The fact that you've realised you have a problem with alcohol and want to change your relationship with it is the first step on the journey, so well done. You're here on this page of the book, which is evidence that you're serious about it – congratulate yourself instead of being critical. You need to treat yourself the same way as you would a good friend. Imagine if they came to you saying they felt terrible because they couldn't stop drinking; you wouldn't be critical of them, would you? No, you would treat them with love and compassion, and remind them how well they were doing for taking the first steps to sobriety. This is how you need to talk to yourself.

'You only fail when you stop trying.'

The same applies if you have a drink at any point, not just at the start. Instead of seeing yourself as a failure, stop and think for a moment. Let's say you've been sober for 55 days and you had one day when you drank; that's a 98 percent success rate. Give yourself a gold star! There's no need to become washed away by feelings of upset and despair. When you become aware that this is what's happening, pause and look at the evidence. Then think about what you would say to a friend who told you the same story.

Having slipped up multiple times myself, I think there are a number of reasons for this we should explore when we look at our approach to quitting. Below are some of the main reasons why I see people slipping up.

We're not sure what we're doing. We decide to stop drinking and then try and white-knuckle it using willpower, but without the right tools or education. This usually leads to a feeling of missing out and we long for the old friend (alcohol) back in our lives, and there's a good chance our sobriety will only be short-term.

We don't plan for our sober journey. I do a lot of marathon running and would never find myself on the start line without having trained for the event. Sobriety is similar in its need for planning, and we should ensure we're prepared for what lies ahead. This can involve writing in our journals, including the pros and cons of drinking and why we're giving it up, as well as thinking about what alcohol-free alternatives to have instead, reading books to expand our knowledge and choosing activities for our extra spare time. We should also keep recording how we feel, take the time to visualise upcoming events, log our progress, and describe how we want ourselves to be in twelve months from now.

We don't look at the data. When we slip up and take a drink, it's important to look at the reasons why. What triggered it to happen? Because when we use slip-ups as a way of working out how to deal with triggers in the future, this is where the learning comes in. There's no need to get emotional – we can get scientific instead and examine the evidence like a detective would investigate a crime scene.

We're not taking account of our habits. It sounds obvious, but if we were drinking in certain situations or at particular locations, it may be best to stay away from them for a while. I used to drink in the evenings in front of the television after my daughter had gone to bed, so I often went to the gym or for a run at that time, and still do; this helped to disrupt my drinking routine. If you feel cravings to drink at certain times of the day, become aware of them and disrupt the thoughts by doing something else. Over time the thoughts about drinking start to fade to almost nothing, they are strongest in the first few weeks.

We don't change our mindset from *can't have a drink* to *don't want one*. This really is the key and I make no apology for repeating it throughout this book because I want to make sure it sticks. Once we change our mindset about giving up the booze it becomes a lot easier, and the chances of drinking again will reduce dramatically. If we take the time to learn about the harm alcohol does and how much better life is without it, our thinking will change and we'll stay on the right path.

We're not excited about becoming sober. Instead, we assume it's a hardship. When I sign up for a marathon I throw myself into the training and focus hard on what lies ahead – the sober journey is similar. There are so many benefits that await us after quitting alcohol, many of which we don't know about at the start. But when we do our research, we gain a good idea about what to expect; this gives us a sense of excitement about all the wonderful things in store for our minds, bodies, and lives. Then sobriety feels like an enjoyable experience of self-discovery and growth, which leads to a higher chance of success.

We fear that life won't be fun any longer. What if our friends don't like us sober? What if we can't do it? What if we end up missing out? What if we fail? The list could go on; the point is that we have to face these fears in order to become sober and – this is the good news – they're never as bad as we imagine. In fact, most of them end up being the complete opposite, especially if we can embrace and enjoy our sober life. Bring it on!

We forget that everything must pass. When we feel down or crave a drink, we forget that the feelings will go and soon we'll feel normal again. Let's not be swept away by the thoughts about drinking that crowd our heads; instead, let's sit back and let them pass by. Meditation is a great tool for managing them.

We don't realise that failure is part of the journey to success. You need to be bad at something before you can become good at it – don't expect perfection right away. Think about the sportspeople who are the best in their field; they don't reach the pinnacle of their chosen sport without failing (often many times) first. If you recognise that slip-ups are part of the learning process, you'll train yourself not to become emotional and upset when they happen. Instead, you can become stronger and use them as an opportunity to learn.

We go it alone. This is where sober groups come in, because we need to be able to share our feelings. We can also help others by talking about our own experiences. In addition to online networks, there are local face-to-face meetings – whatever works best for you. Remember the power of accountability (more in the next chapter about this).

So please don't call yourself a failure; I know from experience how it feels, and it's horrible. Believe me when I say that if you take the time to research, prepare, and embrace sobriety, you will stand a fantastic chance of staying sober long-term. But don't expect to be perfect at the first attempt. This is a journey of learning, and it's guaranteed to have its ups and downs. The good news is that the ups come far more regularly than the downs, so in the end, you're a winner.

'Day 6 – I failed after my day 10, but I feel more positive this time. My mind is clear as I prepare my diary for the week.'
Facebook group post by SK, Tyne and Wear, UK

Chapter 14
I just can't stay accountable

'I want to be accountable to other people, I just don't know how to do it.'

Accountability has always played a huge part in my sober journey, especially in the early days. I found the more people who knew what I was doing, the more I didn't want to let them (or myself) down; it also gave me additional support because there were people to keep an eye on me to ensure I was okay. Thank you to everyone to whom I made myself accountable in those early weeks and months – I can't tell you how much it helped.

So what is accountability? There are two types that I've experienced:

1. When you make yourself accountable to someone and vow you won't let them down by letting yourself down. This is what I did with my wife, family, and closest friends.

2. When you help someone who has the same problem as you, by mentoring them or teaming up together; you're taking on a role that makes you feel responsible. By virtue of the relationship, you become accountable because you want to support them.

Everyone is different in terms of what works for them. I found that I thrived by steadily ramping up the accountability, and then ended up moving to a place where I was helping other people to change their own relationship with alcohol. However, not everyone is comfortable talking openly about their problems with drinking and may not want this kind of pressure; that's completely fine, and you have to do what you feel is right. You don't have to tell the entire world about what you're doing to gain accountability. One great way is to join sober groups, such as the *Be Sober* group on Facebook, and share your story with other people on the same journey; this is a way of making yourself accountable in a safe space and it's just as powerful as doing it in the real world. Don't underestimate the power of Facebook sober groups – the people in them can be your guiding light when you're wandering in a world of darkness.

The 'carrot and stick' accountability approach

A few months ago, I coached a lady who wanted to tell her teenage daughter about her drinking, but was worried about how she might react. She'd got herself into quite a state about having the conversation, so she kept putting it off even though she hadn't had a drink for over a month and was doing brilliantly. I, therefore, suggested that instead of making it a scary and serious conversation, she should rethink her approach and make it fun.

It turned out that her daughter loved nothing more than being taken out to go clothes shopping, so I had the idea that she could make it into a bit of a game and get her daughter involved. The lady told her daughter that if she reached 60 days sober she would take her shopping for new clothes and her daughter could have £50 to spend on them; however, if she slipped up, the budget for clothes would double to £100. Her daughter thought it was great and got really excited about the game. She spent every day supporting her mum, checking up on her and holding her hand through the journey. Not only did it strengthen the bond between mother and daughter, it also made the process easy for them to talk about.

You'll be pleased to know she made it through 60 days with those teenage eyes on her, and is still alcohol-free. I also bet her daughter has been inspired by what she's learned from her mum. Best of all, they had a wonderful shopping trip together!

The fact is that there are plenty of different ways you can make yourself accountable. Telling the whole world can feel scary. Although that also feels like the right thing to do for some of us, just talking to those closest to you might feel right for you. But whatever you choose, do take the time to give it plenty of thought and decide how you're going to make yourself accountable – don't go it alone, because you deserve to have support around you.

Five tips for staying accountable

1. Make a list of everything you have to lose if you start drinking again. While this may sound negative, it also helps you to remain focused on what you've *gained*. It will also prompt you to ask yourself if you want things to return to the way they were before. Chances are your relationships with your family, friends, and children have improved, your performance at work has risen, and your mental health has soared. Do you want to lose all of that for the sake of a drink?

2. Find a partner or mentor. If you're a member of an online sober group, it is fairly easy to find an accountability partner who you can team up with to give mutual support. They're the person you can reach out to if you're having a hard time, experiencing cravings, or thinking about drinking. Some Facebook groups have free mentor programmes to make partnering up a simple process.

3. Tell people. We've covered this already, but I want to reinforce the point. The more people you talk to about what you're doing, the more eyes you're going to have on you. It makes a significant difference, because the support you'll gain will guide you through any difficult times you encounter.

4. Create an accountability statement. Write this down, but make sure you only put what you mean and intend to see through. Mine simply said: 'I will never put alcohol before my daughter, wife and mental health again.' This statement is not open to any form of negotiation, so you have to ensure you can deliver on what you commit to.

5. Celebrate your success. You'll save plenty of money when you stop drinking, so you can celebrate your successes and milestones by planning treats for yourself. I love relaxing spa days as they're a great way to unwind, so I rewarded myself with one after my first 30 days without drinking.

'A friend of mine admitted today that he is struggling with drinking. He sent a message saying he was calling time on his benders. Every time we all go to a gig or a festival we get completely trolleyed and it's become a self-fulfilling prophecy whenever we are together. His message today rang really true to the point that I called him and said:

"You know what mate, my relationship with alcohol is exactly the same – you are not on your own. I have no off switch, I drink until I pass out, I can't have a couple, and I've got a problem."

That's why I've joined this group – I want to get out of this cycle I find myself in. I have a great wife and family, and I love what I do for a living, but I'm a complete failure when it comes to alcohol. I'm feeling anxious and hungover right now due to my activities last night. I have a leaving do tomorrow night and the thought of not having a drink there seems completely crazy. I'm determined not to because I want to change my relationship with drinking.

I hope my ramblings make sense, I guess I wanted to take the first steps and hold myself accountable.'
Facebook group post by LD, Manchester, UK

Chapter 15
I need alcohol to cope with stress

'When I'm stressed I can't resist a drink because it takes the edge off.'

I'm writing this chapter at Rome airport on my way home to London following a fantastic trip with my teenage daughter. We had an amazing week staying in a beautiful loft apartment overlooking the Colosseum, and it was so nice to spend quality time together. My daughter also had the chance to try out her broken Italian language skills on anyone who would listen, which provided me with constant amusement.

I hate airports at the best of times. This one is busy and crowded, and I have beads of sweat on my forehead. I tried hard not to be snappy with my daughter as we wound our way through passport control and security, enduring all the indignities they bring with them – can I have my shoes and belt back, please! After what seemed like an eternity on some uncomfortable plastic seats in an overpriced coffee shop, our call to board was announced and we headed thankfully towards our departure gate to join the queue.

Everything was going well until we settled into our seats on the plane, only to be informed that there was a technical problem. My heart sank and I felt a knot in my stomach. I always try and see the positive in any situation, but I knew we wouldn't be leaving soon. After a long period of wondering what was happening, we were finally told there would be a six-hour delay until a part for the plane could be delivered from Naples in a taxi. What a dismal end to an otherwise perfect week in Italy. I couldn't understand why a huge international airport wouldn't have the aircraft parts they might need closer to hand, and had visions of a taxi driver with a spare engine in the passenger seat and a wing hanging out of the car window, slowly snaking his way through the endless miles of Italian traffic. In the meantime, we were stuck.

After we disembarked the plane, I decided our best bet was to get away from the busy terminal and use the VIP lounge as it would be more comfortable and have better facilities. So my daughter and I headed off and paid the extortionate fee. That brings me to the present moment, laptop open, writing about my experience. I'm feeling stressed out at this point because I just want to get home. I can feel the tension rising and I'm becoming increasingly snappy with my daughter even though she hasn't done anything wrong. Despite the fact that my anxiety has become much better since I quit drinking, it still sometimes seems like it lurks beneath the surface. One drink would bring it bursting back into my life.

The lounge is comfortable with plenty of empty seats, free Wi-Fi, and a huge buffet with all types of food. I guess if we're going to be stuck in the airport for hours then this is the best place we could be, but that doesn't make me any less stressed. Then I remember that airport lounges are renowned for limitless free drinks! I hadn't thought of this when I decided to go inside, so now this is another challenge to deal with.

There it is, right in front of me – I'm looking at it now as I write this. The free bar, with nobody waiting and a bored barman ready to serve people. A huge range of wine, beer, and spirits just a few metres away from the sofa I've sprawled myself across; it would be so easy to get a drink as a 'solution' to my anxiety. Why put a free bar right next to a stressed out ex-enthusiastic wine drinker with six hours to spare? I sometimes wonder if it would be a good idea for me to have a tattoo on my head that says, 'Don't serve me a drink, even if I want one.' That would solve the issue once and for all. I decide against a swift trip to the tattoo parlour, choosing instead to stay where I am and to set up my daughter on her laptop.

Interestingly, when I turn to look at my daughter, I'm surprised to see that she's not stressed at all. She has her laptop out and is using the time to work on her Japanese studies. She's mad about all things Asian and taught herself to speak Japanese at the age of 12. If anything, she seems to see the delay as an opportunity to focus on what she enjoys. Why can't I think like that?

But — and here's the thing — do I feel tempted by that bar? No, and that's the truth. Okay, maybe for the briefest of moments I think a glass of wine would take the edge off of my stress, but I can see that thought for what it is and allow it to pass by. I close my eyes for a few moments and visualise myself four or five hours after I would have downed a bottle (or more) of red wine. I'd be feeling drunk, tired, irritable, and argumentative... and still delayed. It wouldn't be a pretty picture. I know that alcohol won't help and that, sometimes, I simply have to face up to the difficult situations life throws my way.

The truth about alcohol and stress

I can tell you for a fact that it's far easier to manage stress without the false armour of alcohol. Although the flight delay doesn't feel unimportant, I'm still handling it better without a drink because I'm far more present and calm than I would have been with a bottle of wine sloshing around inside me. Life will always serve up challenges, but without alcohol running the show, we feel better equipped to deal with even the worst that the world can throw at us.

There are many situations that can cause stress and make you think a drink would be the perfect solution, so it's worth being prepared and having a set of go-to thoughts in case of an emergency. Here are five techniques you could use when you encounter a challenging situation.

1. Detach yourself. Try and find something to take you away from the situation you're in, either internally or externally. For example, I'm writing this chapter to take my mind off the flight delay, but reading or listening to music could work equally well. Meditation is another way to escape the internal turmoil, and there are some amazing apps you should check out – Calm and Headspace are my personal favourites. If you can physically leave the situation and find some space, all the better.

2. Turn the frown upside down. When you become stressed, it's easy to be irritable and unreasonable. Try to be aware of doing this and catch yourself in the moment. Then pause, step back from the situation, and make a conscious effort to be positive and happy. It makes a real difference to how you feel and will serve to keep you relaxed. If you're a serial stress-head, consider wearing a rubber band around your wrist and twanging it on your skin when you catch yourself becoming moody or grumpy. After a few whacks from the rubber band, you'll soon train yourself to snap out of it and to relax and smile instead.

3. Don't drink alcohol. Okay, this one is really obvious, but you need to keep up your guard. Just reach for the coffee, juice, or alcohol-free drinks instead. You don't want or need alcohol in your life and it certainly won't eliminate the feelings of stress. You may find it blots them out for an hour as you feel the initial euphoria created by the hit of endorphins (the feel-good pleasure chemical produced by our brains when we drink), leading you to drink more in a fruitless attempt to recapture that feeling. Then the stress returns, because it never really went away in the first place. Now as well as feeling anxious you also have an unclear mind, and this is the classic recipe for creating unstable emotions which play havoc with your behaviour. Alcohol takes away a lot more than it gives, and using it to blot out stress is a classic example of this because you never actually deal with the issue – it's always waiting for you once you sober up.

4. Remember it will pass. As with everything, it will come to an end. Almost every stressful situation will pass by at some point (even a long flight delay), so trusting that you'll find yourself on the other side of it is key. Visualise yourself there right now, in peace. In the airport, I imagine myself walking through the front door at home and hugging my wife.

5. Take exercise. This one isn't possible in my situation as I'm stuck at a crowded airport, but a great way of dealing with stressful situations is to pull yourself off the couch and exercise. A session at the gym, a cycle, a run, or a brisk walk will almost always lift your mood and melt away the stressful feelings. It works.

I'm writing the last part of this chapter at home the day after the flight (so it did pass, just like everything does). The delay ended up being ten long hours for a two-hour flight from Rome to London. My daughter and I eventually made it back home at 1:00am, tired and drained, but at least we had our own beds instead of having to sleep at the airport or in a hotel on the outskirts of the city. Another bonus was that I woke this morning without a hangover. That's the final tip for dealing with stress: try and see the positive in the situation.

Hopefully, these stress-busting tips will help ensure you don't think about reaching for alcohol when you're faced with a difficult situation.

'A stressful workday and I'm tired with jet lag. Walked past the pub and had an urge to knock back five pints – my previous response to similar situations. Naively I didn't believe the urge would be so strong at almost five months in. I won't drink but I was very tempted. Urgh.'
Facebook group post by PN, Worthing, UK

Chapter 16
My partner still drinks

'I wish my partner would stop drinking and start encouraging me instead.'

The daily routine was like clockwork. I would head to the shop during the day to ensure I wouldn't run out of wine that evening, then as soon as my daughter had retired to her room the Shiraz would start to flow. Even the process of releasing the cork would instigate a feeling of relaxation. When I eventually went sober and looked back on that, it proved to me how much of my dependency was in my mind. How could I gain a feeling of relaxation just by removing a cork? Alcohol was playing with my feelings without me even drinking any of it.

I used to get snappy when my daughter wouldn't go to bed earlier than usual so I could start drinking sooner; I hate myself for it now, but I wanted her out of the way so that I could get stuck into the wine. I was putting alcohol before the most important people in my life – that's how much power I'd given it. This included my wife, who would often have one or two glasses along with me, then watch me go through the rest of the bottle and start on a new one. She never said anything but, just like the neighbours probably had, she must have noticed the empties clanging in the recycling bin.

When my wife drank with me it made me feel better because I was less aware of exactly how much I had consumed, and I also didn't feel like a lone drinker (although it did make me feel possessive if she had too much of *my* wine). In my heart, I knew I was having most of the booze and that my drinking was out of control, but I carried on for years by pushing the nagging thoughts to the back of my mind.

When I finally found the power to stop drinking, I didn't expect my wife to give up as well. She didn't have a problem, so why should she? This was about me, not her. The last thing I wanted her to think was that I was forcing my new lifestyle on her or judging her for continuing to drink. We spoke in depth about the books I'd read and the path I was choosing to take; she held my hand all the way and was there for me through the highs and the lows. She's been so supportive of my alcohol-free life and I need her around – she's a massive part of my support team. She even thoughtfully volunteered to switch her 'go-to' drink from red wine to Prosecco, as we agreed that having my usual tipple around wasn't a good idea.

Over the first month or two, my wife witnessed the amazing benefits I was gaining from not drinking. While she'd never been a heavy drinker like I was, she decided to cut back anyway and chose only to drink at the weekends (she now drinks Nosecco, a zero percent Prosecco, during the week). When she does drink alcohol she's one of those people who can have a glass or two and stop (why couldn't I have been built like that?). I have no problem whatsoever with her drinking around me – it doesn't make me want to drink as well. I now feel so liberated from alcohol that I sometimes even pour her drink or open the bottle, without any desire to take a sip. This is somewhat unbelievable to me, but if I can do it then – over time – so can you.

My experience of having a partner who still drinks is that I need to accept it. I shouldn't expect her to become sober as it's her choice to do what she wants and I love her no matter what. So long as it's not having a negative impact on us both, there's no problem. The most important aspect for me, especially in the early weeks and months of going sober, was that I put myself first and didn't worry about what anyone else was (or wasn't) doing.

I appreciate I'm lucky because if my wife had, for example, drunk large amounts of my trigger drink (red wine) each night, I'm sure I would have found the sober journey more of a struggle. It might have led to some uncomfortable conversations, as I'd have felt I needed to say something about her cutting back or switching to a different drink.

So what happens when your partner just won't change?

The non-'perfect world' scenario

I believe your partner should be nothing but supportive of you if you've quit alcohol. While they shouldn't feel forced to change their behaviour, if they care about you, they'll make sure they don't do anything to make your life more difficult. Over time they may even reassess how much they're drinking themselves, like my wife did.

Of course, this is a 'perfect world' scenario. I've seen many posts from alcohol-free members of the *Be Sober* group in which they talk about how their partner is still drinking regular excessive amounts and has no intention of changing their ways. I've even read stories about partners being angry because they've lost a drinking buddy, and encouraging their other half to drink with them. This is a difficult situation, because sobriety has to come first and if you're around someone who's toxic it's not going to help.

What's more, if you've tried to quit multiple times before, your partner may think it's just another phase and expect you to fail. Be gentle with them and yourself, because this time you can make a lasting change. The first step is to have a grown-up conversation: explain what you've achieved, how much better your life is now you're not drinking, and that you'd hoped for more encouragement and support on your journey. Don't allow this conversation to turn into an argument. I suggest planning what you're going to say before you say it; write it down, visualising how it will go and the outcome you'd like at the end of it.

It's rare, but if your efforts to talk don't work then it may be worth bringing in some mediation or counselling to dig more deeply into where the problem lies. But please believe me, it's unusual for it to come to this and partners generally do change their views, even if it can take a while.

The key thing to realise is that your partner can still be supportive of you while continuing to drink themselves: helping you on your sober journey is not incompatible with them continuing with their own alcohol consumption. Having said that, from my experience of working with people who've quit alcohol and who have partners who still drink, I'm pleased to confirm that in almost every case, the partner ends up choosing of their own accord to make a change. Sometimes, it can take time and they have to see the transformation appearing in their partner first, but when they do, they become inspired and want a piece of the action.

I can't put a timescale on how long this takes because everyone is different. The most important thing is to never pressure or preach, but to let your actions do the talking – they're far more powerful than being judgy or forcing your views down your partner's throat. I've tried to imagine how I would have reacted if it was my wife who'd quit alcohol and then attempted to make me stop. Of course, I hope that after she'd shone a light on my problem, I would have realised it was the right thing to do for my own good. But in reality, I'm pretty sure I would have fought back until I decided for myself that I needed to quit. The desire to change can only come from within the person who needs to do it – it can't be forced on someone.

'I have not had a drink since the 7th of March. It has not been easy but so worth the fight. It is really nice to remember all of my days. I have so much more energy and I wake up feeling refreshed. My kids are proud of me but they are asking why dad has not stopped drinking.

I did not realise how bad it was. Today, I had to pick my husband up off the ground from the front of the house where he fell asleep looking under the car. I was so embarrassed, as our front faces the rest of our condo neighbours.

Any suggestions as to how to get him to see what this is doing to our family? This is not the first time, but it is the first time I have seen it being sober.' – Facebook group post by SH

'I've recently had my wedding anniversary and it got me thinking about my relationships and how drastically things have changed since I stopped drinking. This is my first sober boyfriend – my husband.

We met when I was three years alcohol-free. After I gave up the booze, I was single for three years. All my relationships had been draining, unbalanced and dysfunctional when I drank. After giving up, I realised that alcohol had always been a third party in each of those relationships. No wonder nothing ever worked for me! I would make one wrong choice after another and tell myself I attracted horrible partners. When I got sober I realised that I CHOSE each and every one of them. They all drank too much as well – obviously!!

When alcohol was out of my system and out of my life, I finally took the time to figure out what I wanted from a relationship. It took a while to get that clarity, but it was worth it. Some things can't be rushed. My husband is my first sober choice and every day proves that it was the right choice. I told him that I'd had a drinking problem on our second date and it was not an issue for him. He asks me to this day if it's OK for him to have a beer at home. I appreciate it so much, even though the answer in 99 percent of cases is yes. Give it time. Let yourself recover a bit more. Take time to figure out what you want. It's worth it.'
Facebook group post by AC, Portsmouth, UK

Chapter 17
I can't socialise without alcohol

'If I quit drinking, I won't have a social life.'

For almost all my adult life, just about every social occasion involved drinking. The thought of going out with friends for an evening without sinking a few pints of beer or glasses of wine seemed ridiculous – why would anyone do that? There was no point going if alcohol wasn't involved. Of course, I couldn't stop drinking after a few pints of beer – once I started I was on a mission to put away as many as I could, as quickly as possible. What's more, whenever I went out for the evening drinking with friends I would always make sure there was a bottle of red wine waiting at home for a nightcap. I even remember evenings when I got back so drunk the room would be spinning, but I'd still break the wine open and keep going. This resulted in numerous visits to the bathroom to be sick (assuming I actually made it there) as well as some fairly painful falls up the stairs as I attempted to make my way to bed in the early hours. Not that I felt any pain at the time, but the bumps and bruises the next morning gave me a visual reminder that my drinking was out of control.

I used to laugh at people who didn't drink. I believed they were missing out and had boring, sad little lives lacking in happiness and enjoyment. How wrong I was, because since I stopped I've discovered that in social situations, I can have just as much fun (in fact, more) when I'm sober.

It took me a while to learn this, though. In the month after I quit, I chose to avoid every social situation at which drink might be involved; I'd committed myself to a sober life but was still fragile and finding my feet. Mixing with heavy drinkers and people who thought it would be a good idea to encourage me to drink was not a good idea at this stage. By the way, I'm not suggesting you have to stay away from all socialising – that's just what I did because it made sense for me. You need to decide what's right for you, and by thinking about it ahead of time you'll ensure you're prepared.

It ended up taking around three months before I felt ready to venture into an environment where the drink would be flowing. When the evening of the first social outing came I was really nervous, but I felt prepared and even enjoyed myself (leaving at 10:30pm when the drunk people started to become loud, annoying, and repetitive). After the first social event was out of the way, I felt more relaxed and have been out many times since then. However, I still avoid certain friends who I know might pressure me to drink, and there are particular locations that don't appeal to me as a non-drinker, so I stay away. I've found that some social events just aren't worth attending after all. Who knew?

My work Christmas party is an example of how socialising has become a pleasure since giving up alcohol. Everyone was so drunk I was able to quietly slip off and drive myself home at midnight. Nobody even noticed. I still had a turn on the dancefloor and plenty of laughs and good conversations, but once everyone was drunk, it wasn't much fun anymore and I enjoyed having the freedom of leaving when I wanted.

Whenever I attend a social event at which I know drink will be flowing, I go armed with a plan, and I've found the best strategy is visualisation. Beforehand, I create a clear picture in my mind of how the evening will go. I visualise everything, from what I'm wearing, through to walking through the door, to being offered my first drink. I play it like a movie in my head, and arm myself with what I'll say when I'm offered a drink and how the conversation will go. I've found this strategy to be incredibly effective; in the early days, I'd write my vision of the event in my journal and then compare it with the reality the next day.

Another helpful strategy is to find out ahead of time if there will be suitable alcohol-free drinks available. If not, I often take my own. I also keep an eye on my glass to make sure I don't pick up the wrong one. If you are asked about your dietary requirements ahead of an event you can write 'I don't drink alcohol' on your response.

Friendships and alcohol

My experience has highlighted the fact that many of my friendships were based around drinking. If this is the case for you too, you may find these friends react badly to you going sober because, as they see it, they've lost a drinking buddy. They might also think their own behaviour is being judged. So you may have to ask yourself if these are true friendships, or whether you just had a common love of alcohol. Proper friends will be supportive of your new sober lifestyle and would never consider trying to make you have a drink.

You could also find that you start spending less time with some of your old drinking buddies because you don't share the same interests any longer. On the flip side, you'll also find new friends with whom you can probably form much stronger relationships.

That said, a couple of my biggest drinking friends have actually quit drinking after seeing the positive changes I've made to my life, and our relationships are now better than ever. We go running instead of drinking these days.

Because alcohol is no longer in charge and we're picking and choosing what we do with our social life, it's natural to explore new interests. The best thing of all is that we now do everything with a clear mind, and find ourselves fully present when we go out socially. Because we aren't drunk, we get to remember everything.

After a few months without drinking, I found that I was extra motivated to get out and explore new interests. I've been travelling more, blogging more, and spending way more time with my daughter (without snapping and arguing with her). I have so much energy to do things that I regularly go to the gym and run it off. I've even made connections in the sober world through online groups and real-world events, and have found these friendships to be far more honest and true because they are not based around drinking. In fact, I now find myself with the best social life I've had in over two decades.

'Day 534.

Yesterday me and the bearded one hosted a barbecue (in the rain!) for my niece's 15th birthday. It was chaotic, noisy, wet, messy and absolutely brilliant. All the family that could make it came and we all chipped in with food and made the day a special one for my niece who is growing into one hell of a beautiful, sweet-natured, naturally cool and talented young woman. There were big belly laughs, and deep meaningful conversations, wistful rememberings and mutual feelings of nostalgia. No drama, no spite, no tears or tantrums. The day turned to evening and with full tummies and aching grins we said long-drawn-out goodbyes in the typical British style of saying "right, I'm off" every 5 minutes until finally leaving an hour later.

It was only towards the end that I realised that not one person had drunk an alcoholic drink at all throughout the entirety of the celebrations. There had been no need. Our good cheer came from the vibe that I'm proud my family and I were able to create in my garden in spite of the miserable weather. Our perseverance in the damp weather paid off as the sun came out in the evening and dried out the garden enough for us to have a fire for the children to roast marshmallows over and feast in the excitement of playing in the *dark past bedtime, while the remaining grown-ups rewarded our hard work with tea and leftover cake (that might have just been me).*

It was midnight by the time I snuggled into bed, my hair still smoky from the fire pit and ears buzzing from the noise of the day. I anticipated having a difficult time getting to sleep after being so wired from laughter, conversation and sugar. But my happy, sleepy brain mellowed into slumber as soon as my head hit the pillow. A rarity for me indeed.

I never tire of waking up on a sunny morning after a good night free from a hangover, feeling rested and happy to reflect over the evening's events without the beer fear clawing through my chest and my brain, or searching my memory for snatches of regretful conversations and actions that I'd soon need to plan redemption for. Stretching out in bed this morning, I savoured that wholesome feeling while the kids slept on through their sugar hangover, feeling grateful for the stronger connections I now have with my family, and the work we're all putting in separately and together to be better in ourselves and together.

I love my bat shit crazy family. They're hard work, they're complicated, often strange, sometimes drama queens, but always mine. There may be a lot of things we would all choose to change about our family history, but I'm proud of where we've been, and optimistic about where we're heading.'
Facebook group post by Amy Louise Harding-Smith, UK

'5 months ago today I took my last sip of alcohol. I have gained so much strength and self-respect. I would never have thought just by quitting alcohol I would feel the way I do. Sobriety suits my personality, I love sober me. I hated myself when I was drinking but I never knew why. Now I do, because alcohol had no positive benefits – I can't even think of one.

The amount of times I've made a complete arse of myself because I drank to get drunk. I don't ever want to go back there. The only times I've been tempted to drink over the last 5 months is at events with other drinkers (a wedding and a music concert). I felt self-conscious and thought I would be more relaxed in this environment if I had a drink. That helped me to realise that when I did use alcohol I would feel nervous, drink, and then carry on and drink waaaay too much, ending up hating myself the next day because I would have humiliated myself in some way. I was sick of the aftermath of drinking, which is why I eventually quit. My goal is to enjoy parties, concerts and festivals without the alcohol that gave me fake confidence. The longer I go without alcohol the stronger and happier I am. I feel like my life has just begun and what a great feeling that is.

I love this group... it's so inspiring.'
Facebook group post by VJ, 45, Bournemouth, UK

Chapter 18
Surely I can't have a sober holiday?

'Vacations and drinking go hand in hand. I won't enjoy a holiday without alcohol.'

It goes without saying that sober holidays can feel like a challenge. Vacations are seen as a time to let your hair down and relax, and of course, you probably associate that with drinking. In fact, you might see it as an opportunity to drink way more than you would normally do at home. I often see holiday-makers quaffing beer and wine before midday – even at breakfast time, which is something I imagine they would never do if they weren't abroad. I was never a big daytime drinker even when I was on holiday, but I made up for it as soon as the sun went down.

When I look back at the holidays I went on before I stopped drinking, I'm met with a stark reminder of how alcohol was in charge of my life. Before a trip away I'd worry that I might not be able to get my hands on my beloved red wine as soon as I arrived, so I'd search on Google to ensure there were shops nearby to stock up. When my teenage daughter and I travelled to Tokyo on a trip of a lifetime, for instance, the first thing I did after I'd dumped our luggage in the apartment was to head out and find a shop. I thought that as long as I disguised the trip as being part of our initial reconnaissance of the area, I wasn't a bad dad.

If I feared the shops might let me down, I'd stash alcohol in my suitcase as a backup plan; I didn't care for customs rules and regulations, because alcohol came first. I even remember having my suitcase searched by some stern looking security guards at Dubai airport. They weren't impressed when they pulled out a box of red wine, although they did let me keep it! This summed up my addiction; I was more worried about not having my daily wine fix than I was about being arrested.

In those days, I could never have believed a holiday would be more fun without alcohol involved, but once I experienced the joy of time with my family when I was fully present and engaged, it was a revelation to me and I never looked back. Now, the joy of spending time with my daughter and not needing to work out how I'm going to have a drink is wonderful. I'm not watching the clock or ending fun times early to uncork my wine; I'm totally absorbed in the moment and loving every minute.

If you've stopped drinking and have a holiday coming up, you need to plan ahead and approach it with the right mindset. You don't want to feel like you're missing out because you aren't drinking; instead, you should feel like you don't want a drink because alcohol is irrelevant to your life. You'll have a good time without needing to drink, trust me on this. Given how much of this book you've read, there's every chance you're feeling strong enough to enjoy a holiday sober and I'm certain you'll have a much better time without booze.

I know I've mentioned mindset a few times throughout this book, but this repetition is intentional because changing your mindset really is the key to finding peace in a life without alcohol. So I make no apology for reminding you of this and pushing you to do the work to change your beliefs from feeling like you *can't have a drink* to feeling like you *don't want one*. When you feel like this, it becomes so much easier and you'll find holidays to be the best they've ever been.

Practical tips for sober holidays

Below are the main challenges I've found on vacation, along with my advice on how to deal with them.

You're offered after-dinner free drinks and shots in restaurants. A polite 'no thanks' does the trick. If you feel you need an excuse then 'I'm on medication so I can't drink' works in most cases. Although I've always preferred to be honest and tell people that I don't drink because it does nothing for me, sometimes it can be easier to make up a reason.

Your travel companions are drinking. You need to be clear and tell them you aren't drinking ahead of the holiday. Set boundaries and expectations, and if they're true friends they'll support you.

Everyone everywhere is drinking. Good for them, but you're not and you should be proud of being different. Embrace the sober life and enjoy your freedom. The absence of holiday hangovers is wonderful – you can get up at sunrise and walk along the beach while everyone else is sleeping off their sore heads or regretting their behaviour from the night before. Make the most of the new opportunities sobriety gives you.

Lack of decent alcohol-free drinks. Depending on your destination you'll probably find that most European countries and the USA have a good supply of alcohol-free beer, juices, tonics, and mixers. I found the Caribbean and Asia to be lacking in decent alternative drinks, although after a few days of searching in Barbados, I found one called Kola Tonic which tasted amazing when mixed with ginger ale. This is stocked all over the Caribbean. Try to see your holiday as an opportunity to explore new and exciting drinks; there are some incredible alcohol-free alternatives if you take the time to search. Make it part of your adventure.

You keep thinking about drinking instead of enjoying yourself.
Forget it – you don't drink now, so there's nothing to think about.
You made the firm decision to quit, so move on. Just let the
thoughts pass, surf any urges, and get on with enjoying your
holiday. You don't need alcohol in your life and it certainly won't
make you have a better holiday. If the thoughts don't pass quickly
or keep coming back, spend some time meditating or take a walk to
disrupt them. They'll fade away before you know it.

*'I'm currently on holiday in Greece, and it's my first ever all-inclusive
holiday. As I've been alcohol-free for just over seven months now, I
thought that I would find it easy, but seriously I'm not!! How can
this be after seven months? Yesterday, I told myself I could just have
a beer, it wouldn't hurt, would it? After all, I am on holiday!! Next, I
sought approval from my wife (who still drinks), and at first she
suggested that I didn't have one, but then when I told her I'd just
stick to beer, and maybe an odd cocktail, but no wine (my old
poison), she told me she'd leave it up to me and it was my choice.
Next, I sought approval from my daughter, who was fine with me
having whatever I wanted. So, there I was all geared up as I
wandered up to the bar to get my wife a Tequila Sunrise and myself
a beer. But on the bar was a jug of lemon and lime infused water. I
stopped and thought how refreshing it looked. I then told myself
why not just have a glass of that water for now, then after that, if I
still fancied a beer, go back and get one. So that's what I did! As I
lay on the sun lounger drinking my water, I still felt like having a
beer, but after my "near miss", I told myself something that a lot of
people use in this group... JUST FOR TODAY.'*
Facebook group post by Graham, UK

*'Halfway through my sober solo holiday in Greece and I'm smashing
it!!! Feel so healthy and relaxed. I never dreamed I could enjoy a
holiday without alcohol. Funny thing is now, I can't imagine drinking
it!*
Facebook group post by Alison, USA

On my first alcohol-free holiday as an adult. Normally by now, I would be itching to go to the surf club across the road for a bottle of wine with dinner (roll home and have a second) but instead, I am chilling on the balcony with an alcohol-free beer while hubby has gone to pick up a takeaway, and after dinner it is board games with the kids. Some might say boring... I say perfect.'
Facebook group post by Sara, Australia

Chapter 19
I can't deal with bad feelings without a drink

'Alcohol helps me deal with challenging emotions; without it I wouldn't be able to cope.'

I always used to find an excuse to drink. Whether I'd had a good day, a bad day, or an indifferent day, I managed to find a reason. But I definitely found it easier to justify drinking when I was experiencing some kind of emotional upset. I'd drink so I could forget for a few hours whatever it was that had made me feel bad, then stumble into bed and have a night of restless, broken sleep while my head spun like an overloaded washing machine.

Did the alcohol solve my problem? No, it simply moved it out of sight for a bit; I never faced up to the actual issue that was causing me fear, pain, worry, or anger. To make matters worse, I'd wake up with a hangover which would cause my anxiety to go through the roof, putting me in an even worse mood. It's rather like the way in which a payday loan company solves a short-term cash shortage, but makes you pay it back with interest. I'd drink again to feel better, and the vicious cycle of drinking, suppressing the emotion, and being grumpy would go on and on.

The fact is that the car bumper stickers are true: 'shit happens'. There's no avoiding it, and if we go through life pretending we won't face challenges and tough times we're being totally unrealistic.

Now, without alcohol in my life, I have to handle my emotions and reactions raw and real, because I'm no longer thinking with a brain infused with Shiraz. While this sounds difficult, I actually find myself so much better equipped to deal with problems because I feel mentally resilient and tough. Annoyances that used to cause me to have a meltdown don't phase me any longer, or not to nearly the same extent as before. Once the problem is dealt with, I can consider the matter closed and don't need to dwell on it – I haven't hidden it away, ready for it to reappear later on.

When we don't drink, we're so much more aware of our feelings, so we quickly know if something is causing us pain. The false armour of alcohol isn't blurring the picture. This makes it relatively easy to solve a problem quickly in a calm way, before it gets out of hand. With a little practice, you too can train yourself to handle uncomfortable emotions without the need to drink.

The truth about uncomfortable feelings

I've found that by accepting the following beliefs, I've built up a great ability to handle situations that would have previously caused an emotional reaction.

Nothing is permanent. Including emotions – they come and go, a bit like clouds passing across the sky. At the time, it can feel like a bad feeling might never pass, but it will.

Negative emotions are necessary. This is because they can help you to learn and grow stronger. Everyone has them at times.

You can't block negative emotions. Accept that you'll experience them sometimes. When you fight or block them it can actually make them worse; instead, learn to be aware of them, and mindful about how you allow them to affect you.

Over time, I've learned to watch my emotions without judgement, observing them as if I'm on the bank of a fast-flowing river. The rapids are my thoughts and feelings, and I simply watch them passing by. I never step into the water and allow them to wash me away.

Another strategy is to apply labels to your emotions when they come up. This can help you to bring them into the light, become curious about them, and see them for what they are. Keep the labels simple and observe the emotion calmly: 'sadness' or 'guilt' for example. This is a powerful technique and if you use it you'll soon find yourself becoming tuned in to your feelings.

If I find myself with a head full of challenging thoughts and emotions, I'll often turn to meditation and mental imagery. I close my eyes for a few minutes, calm my mind, and empty my head before visualising a sky. The clouds in the sky are my feelings, and I observe them moving past without judgement. Once the sky is clear, I gently open my eyes and return to my day feeling refreshed and calm.

Given that everybody has to handle negative emotions from time to time, it's well worth taking the time to find a strategy that works for you. You need to be equipped to deal with them without drinking.

'Tonight, I had a bad day. I had an argument with my ex-husband and an argument with my boyfriend, and the first thing I did was go to the shop. I spent about 10 minutes looking at the alcohol because I felt like I needed it to settle my emotions so I could get to sleep tonight. I kept picking up bottles of wine and putting them back. I wanted anything to take the pain away. I ended up buying a packet of salted peanuts, tonic water and diet coke. I got home and felt restless and deflated. I was and am yearning for something to numb the pain. If I had a drink, I would have sent messages to them both but I haven't done either. I'm messaging on here instead. I need to learn that alcohol won't fix my problems or take away the pain, it

will make it a million times worse the next day. A small thing to a lot of people but a big win to me.'
Facebook group post by JL, Nottingham, UK

Chapter 20
I can't talk to my kids about my drinking

'My children have seen me drinking for years; there's no point changing now, the damage is already done.'

I speak to many parents who are worried about talking to their children about their issues with drinking. They're often scared that their kids have been damaged by their behaviour, and think they're too far down the line to make a positive change. The damage to their children has already been done.

Let me tell you that if you're thinking like this, you're wrong.

It's a fact that our children learn from us and copy our behaviour, and that includes the way we act around alcohol. I'm a perfect example of this. My dad drank red wine in front of me on most days and I ended up doing exactly the same because I thought it was grown-up, sophisticated, and cool. However, a couple of weeks after I quit drinking, I sat down with my daughter who was 13 at the time, and explained to her that alcohol was playing too large a part in my life. I confessed that I was putting drinking ahead of the most important things to me, and that I'd decided to make a change: I wouldn't be drinking any longer. I also shared with her what I'd learned from the sober books I'd read, and armed her with the facts about alcohol so that she was well placed to make her own decisions as she went forward in life.

My daughter takes things in her stride, and like most teenagers, initially reacted rather indifferently to this. But after we spoke further she opened up and said that my decision made perfect sense to her – why would I keep drinking if it was causing me so many issues? She also told me I was snappy, unreasonable, and argumentative when I'd been drinking. I assured her this was going to change.

As I mentioned before, being sober is the gift that keeps on giving. A couple of days after I spoke to my daughter about why I quit drinking, she came running into the kitchen and informed me that she'd downloaded a sober 'day counter' app on her phone. When I asked her why, she said that because I'd quit alcohol she was going to quit fizzy soda drinks too! I thought this was really sweet and felt incredibly touched that I'd inspired her in some (strange) way. She still has the app on her phone to this day (she's had a couple of slip-ups involving Dr Pepper, but she learned from her mistakes and has grown stronger for it). I found it fascinating that she'd been touched like this.

That conversation was so important, because it changed everything. I'd bared my soul to my daughter. By the time we finished talking she was incredibly supportive of what I was doing, and could understand why I needed to quit. I'm sure she respected me for being open and vulnerable, as well as for including her and considering her feelings.

How to involve your kids

If you have a teenage child like me and you're worried about how they might feel about your relationship with alcohol, my advice is to sit down with them and talk. Simply tell them the truth, and I'm almost certain you'll find accountability and support. If you have younger children, I believe you should speak to them in a way that serves to make them feel totally safe. At the same time, you can allow them to express any fears or other feelings they may have. I know it can seem hard to have this kind of conversation (admitting you aren't perfect to someone who looks up to you is never comfortable). But believe me, you'll earn an incredible amount of respect and your kids will sit up and pay attention to what you're doing.

It can also be fun to involve them in the sober journey, and to get them excited by including them in things like treats for your sober milestones. Before you know it, you'll have a valuable support crew willing you on to success. If you have a child in your house with the promise of a trip to a theme park when you reach 30 days alcohol-free, they're going to do all they can to make sure you don't have a drink, and you won't want to let them down either.

Now you may be thinking that all this makes sense in principle, but does it really work? I can tell you from personal experience that it does, and here's why.

A few months ago my daughter was staying at a friend's house and I received the following text just before midnight: 'Hi dad, just to let you know Ellie has got out a bottle of gin and is drinking. I'm not touching it, not interested and I wouldn't want to let you down x.'

Now, I'm not saying my daughter will never drink; she'll no doubt go on her own journey and I'm pretty sure she'll explore where alcohol fits into her life. But I'm certain that if I hadn't changed my relationship with alcohol, and if I hadn't had the open conversations with her, there's a high chance she would have drunk that gin and who knows where that would have led. I've armed her with the facts, made her think about alcohol from a new perspective, and hopefully set her up for success when it comes to making sensible decisions about drinking in the future.

Given that she's seen me from both sides – the boozy dad and the sober dad – we often speak about my decision to remove alcohol from my life. She recently told me in no uncertain terms that she much prefers the alcohol-free version, and when I asked her why, she said it was because I'm much calmer, less moody, and more fun to be around these days. The great thing is that I also enjoy her company more, because I'm present and engaged when we do things together. Our relationship is the best it's ever been and is going from strength to strength.

So do take the time to talk to your kids. It may help to plan what you're going to say in advance, but I assure you it's one of the most positive and powerful things you can do on this journey. Your children can form your greatest support team – being accountable to them is a huge motivator.

'I made it!! Doesn't mean it was easy... but this kid... this child of mine inspires me to be better every single day. To tell me how proud she is of me, she got me gifts and wrote me a very sweet card. For a few days last week, I actually contemplated moderation. I'm so glad I didn't give in!! Because...
I DON'T DRINK ANYMORE!!!!!
If I can do it, YOU CAN DO IT!!'
Facebook group post by CS, Gainesville VA, USA

Chapter 21
It's too difficult on blue days without a drink

'I need alcohol to help get me through the tough days.'

If you've been a heavy drinker for years, like I used to be, there's every chance that after a few weeks of not drinking you'll start to feel incredibly happy. You may even wonder why you feel like that – I know I did, because I couldn't understand why I was laughing and smiling so much. It was a weird feeling and one I hadn't experienced for a long, long time.

This 'happy' stage is often referred to as the 'pink cloud' period and it feels wonderful; it comes about because we're returning to our natural baseline of happiness. This is the 'normal' amount of happiness we feel continuously through our lives, and the level to which we eventually return whenever we've experienced an especially high or low moment. When we drink heavily, alcohol robs us of our happiness and we never manage to return back to our true baseline. Then the more we drink the further we creep away from where our happiness level should be, which is why we can feel sad and depressed when we drink every day. From the Facebook group members that I've worked with, it seems the heavier drinkers feel the highest levels of happiness when they quit. The good news is that this happy feeling stays long-term.

So there I was, a couple of months into sobriety, and experiencing levels of joy that I hadn't known since I was a child. The whole world was tinted with sunshine and sparkles – it was amazing. Then I woke up one morning and the happiness seemed to have vanished. Where had it gone? I felt incredibly sad and low, as if the sun that had been shining into my life had experienced a total eclipse. I just wanted to cry, and ended up sitting in bed in an awful mood questioning everything about my life. It would have been easy to have reached for a drink.

Thankfully, I'd read about the 'blue day' blips and was prepared for them. Instead of uncorking a bottle of wine, I weathered the storm and am pleased to report that within 24 hours the sun was back out and shining into my life – my smile had returned.

Post-Acute Withdrawal Symptoms (PAWS)

What I experienced was one of the Post-Acute Withdrawal Symptoms (PAWS). These usually crop up around four to six weeks after quitting drinking, as your brain goes through the healing and rebalancing process. This causes a kind of lag that can make you feel like you're dancing for joy one minute and sends you crying into your breakfast cereal the next. Common symptoms that I've known people to experience include: feelings of depression, anxiety, sleeplessness, lack of concentration, low motivation, memory loss, low energy, and a general feeling of sadness.

However, you can take comfort in the fact that these are only temporary, and are a clear sign that your mind and body are healing. I only experienced a handful of days when I felt really down, and didn't have any after the first two or three months.

Just by reading this chapter you're armed and aware. If you experience feelings like this you don't need to worry, simply ride them out and they should fade away as quickly as they arrived. Take it as a positive that you're recovering and rebalancing.

As well as PAWS, we have to face up to the fact that normal life can present us with challenges. We can also just feel down without any good reason. Not every day will be sunshine and roses, and it's worth having some tactics to deal with the bad ones. They always pass, and you'll find yourself bouncing back to your baseline level of happiness pretty quickly.

Below are five techniques I use if I find myself feeling down, and they each help me to get back in the right frame of mind. It's worth making a list of the things that work for you, and if you experience a low mood take a moment to pause, look at your list, and deploy your best tactic to combat it.

Ways to deal with blue days

Pause and reflect. Whenever I experience a low mood, I try to acknowledge how I feel, then take a moment to stop, reflect, and question why. The process of pausing and becoming curious about your feelings can lift you back into a place of positivity.

Talk to someone. A problem aired is a problem halved, so talking about your feelings with someone who cares is a fantastic way to get support. We often fuel low feelings with negative self-talk, so by speaking to a friend or loved one, we can gain a more balanced and logical view without the negativity.

Get your journal out. Your journal should become your new best friend because writing down your feelings is such a helpful way of exploring them. Seeing them in black and white allows you to take stock from a new perspective and be curious about them. What's more, you'll often find that the process of transferring your negative feelings from inside your head onto the paper makes them start to fade away – it's like you've got everything off your chest.

Disrupt the feelings. If you're sitting at home feeling down and in a bad mood, I suggest disrupting the feelings by leaving the situation. Get out of the house and take some fresh air; the options are almost endless but my favourites include taking a brisk walk, going for a run, or heading out on my bike into the woods.

Practice gratitude. This is a fantastic way to pause and reflect on the positive things in your life. Write down three to five things you're grateful for (they don't have to be expensive or material things). This will show you that nothing is lacking in your life, and you have everything you need. I try and do this at least once a week.

'Struggling with everything today, feeling down.'
Facebook group post by SB, Melbourne, Australia

'Just don't drink!! It will make it worse. Even though that conniving voice tells you otherwise, it's a liar!! I listened to it too many times. It gets easier. Even sober, we have bad days. It always gets better!!'
Facebook group post by Melissa, USA

Chapter 22
I still think about drinking

'After all this time, will I ever stop thinking about having a drink?'

One of the most common questions I'm asked by people who quit alcohol is: 'How long will it take for me to stop thinking about drinking?' This is understandable, because we want to feel at peace rather than being dogged by the thoughts that pop up encouraging us to slip up. In fact, most people who choose an alcohol-free life think about drinking regularly in their first weeks and months.

I won't tell you it's a bed of roses: the first week or two can feel pretty tough. We're making a huge change to our lives and will be thinking about (and possibly craving for) alcohol quite often. We're also faced with an element of uncertainty about how long this will go on for – how many weeks or months it will be until we're in a calm and happy place where thoughts about alcohol no longer come to mind.

This will get better over time, but it's important to realise that we'll probably always have the occasional impulse to drink. I know people who've been sober for decades, and they still have those thoughts every now and then. However, they know that's all they are – thoughts. And that they'll pass. Most importantly, they don't react to or act upon them.

My advice is to accept the thoughts, observe them, and allow them to simply pass on by. You can also read chapter 21, which contains techniques for learning to observe thoughts and feelings without judgement. The main thing is not to become swept away by them.

You're on a journey

When we're at the start of the journey to alcohol freedom it can feel pretty daunting, because we have a mountain to climb but can't see where the summit is. We know it's the place where we'll find freedom and happiness, if only we could haul ourselves up there to plant the flag on the peak. Sometimes our mind plays tricks on us as we work out how hard and far the trek is going to be. To make matters worse, the clouds are low down the mountainside, so it's impossible to see the summit; each time we round a corner we're disappointed to discover we're not as far as we thought.

However, I can tell you right now that the climb is really not too hard, and we can all get to the top – we just can't see it at the start. If you've reached this far you've probably equipped yourself with the right tools and equipment to make the climb. You know that having the right mindset, a strong support network, and a determination to succeed are what will carry you to the summit.

What's more, I only know a handful of people who've made it to the top on the first attempt. Most of us who want to quit drinking and attempt this climb need a few tries, and we'll fall down many times and dent our pride. But we reach further each time we start again, and before long we find ourselves getting closer and closer to an alcohol-free life. The summit seems so far away when you begin, but once you've made it past the first base camp you can start to see it's only a few hundred metres away – you just have to navigate the tricky section of uncertainty that you are faced with when you started.

I found the first month or two of my journey towards alcohol freedom felt very much like I was doing this hike, without knowing how long it was going to take. I spent a lot of time wondering when I would stop thinking about drinking and feel free. But after the first couple of months, the peak came through the clouds and everything started to become so much easier. I found myself thinking less about drinking, and as my brain re-calibrated, I began feeling more positive, grounded, and mentally tough.

It took me three or four months to reach the top of the mountain and finally stop thinking about drinking. I'd mastered a life without alcohol. Yes, I still had the odd thought here and there, and imagine I always will. For example, if I went past an inviting looking pub on a summer's day I might for a moment consider sitting in the garden with a long pint of beer. But I know these are just thoughts and nothing more; I have thousands of transient thoughts every day that I don't act on, so why should 'I want a drink' be any different?

Once I reached the point at which I was only thinking about drinking once or twice a week at the very most, I wrote down some of the thoughts I used to have about alcohol:

- Do I have enough wine for the evening? Should I buy two more bottles in case I run out?
- Does the guy on the supermarket checkout notice how much wine I buy? This is the fourth time this week he's served me.
- How long is it until I can start drinking?
- Just go to bed so I can get stuck into this bottle of wine. (To my daughter.)
- Can we get work out of the way? I want to go home and drink.
- Do the neighbours notice how many empty wine bottles are in my recycling bin?
- I wish this hangover would clear – that's okay, it'll fade away when I have the first glass of wine.
- My anxiety is all over the place today, but that bottle of wine will calm it all down.
- (On the morning school run.) I wonder if I'm over the drink-drive limit because of the wine I had the night before?
- I wonder if people can smell the alcohol on my breath? (At work.)

I'm so thankful my mind is no longer full of thoughts like this.

Below are the five stages I experienced on the path to mastering a sober life.

1. Unawareness. You don't even know you have a problem. So many people are stuck here and never get past this place. If you're different, congratulate yourself.

2. Awareness. This is the point at which you've realised you have a problem that's causing you internal conflict, but you don't know how to fix it. This is the most painful step on the path to sobriety but don't worry, you don't stay here for long.

3. Education. You start to learn about the issues and solutions – it's all about educating yourself and changing your beliefs. I launched into sobriety like I was studying for a university degree. I read every book I could lay my hands on, joined Facebook groups (and even started my own), watched videos, and signed up to online courses. I wanted to learn everything there was to know about the tools and tactics for going sober. Take the time to learn all this stuff – some advice is better than the rest and different people like different things, so explore as much as you can.

4. Action. This is when you do something positive to make a change, by putting your education into practice. You start to experience life without alcohol involved, and begin to understand that it really is better without the booze. A great example is that I didn't used to 'believe' it was possible to go to a party and have fun without drinking – how wrong I was. That would never have shifted until I'd experienced it for myself in the real world.

5. Mastery. This is when you're are truly free and alcohol no longer runs the show. This stage took me a good three to four months to achieve, and only comes through changes in your beliefs combined with real-world experiences. Once you're here, you'll have switched your mindset from *can't have a drink* to *don't want one* and will experience total freedom.

'I use a skill called "opposite action" when I start thinking about drinking. Hop in the shower, go for a walk, meet someone for coffee, watch a scary movie, etc. Do the opposite of what your actions at the time want you to do! Hope this helps!'
Facebook group post by EJ, Ottawa, ON, Canada

'How long does it take for the "if only I could have a drink" thoughts to go from your head???'
Facebook group post by MW, Milton Keynes, UK

Chapter 23
I can't stop being harsh on myself

'I'm a failure – I just can't do this.'

When we go sober, we often start from a place of low self-worth because we feel so bad about our drinking. Then, as we travel along the sober journey with all its slip-ups and setbacks, we can make life even harder by blaming ourselves for our problems and being negative about what we can achieve. Unsurprisingly, this makes us more likely to give up trying than if we'd been kind to ourselves and been able to think positive thoughts. Let's explore how this works.

Self-criticism

If your best friend had quit drinking and told you that, after a month of being sober, they felt a complete failure because they'd had a beer at the weekend, would you:

A) Agree and tell them they'd let themselves down.
B) Point out that what they've achieved is amazing (one drinking day out of 30 is a 97 percent success rate), and that slip-ups are an opportunity to learn, understand, and grow stronger. You'd also offer them some support and unconditional friendship.

I'm pretty sure you'd go with the second option, wouldn't you? And yet when we talk to ourselves, we often choose the first. We humans can be really hard and unreasonable on ourselves, and this can be damaging to our well-being. I used to do it all the time, and would often end up convincing myself that I couldn't achieve my goal or that I wasn't worthy enough to live a sober life. But over time, I learned to catch myself whenever negative self-talk started up. I was able to say, 'Stop. Now talk to yourself like you would to a friend.' This worked incredibly well for me, and I soon began to change the way that I related to my thoughts; this meant the messages from my mind became more positive.

So next time you start talking to yourself in a harsh way, try and catch yourself in the act and become aware of it. Then change what you're saying and become your own best friend instead.

Negative thinking

I hear statements like this all the time:

'I can never quit drinking. I've always been like this and will never change.'
'I'm a failure – I just can't stop drinking.'
'I'm going to a party at the weekend; I know I'll drink – I've already made up mind.'
'If I keep drinking I know I'll end up with serious health problems, but I can't stop.'

All of the statements above (and many more like them) come from a default position of automatic negative thinking. This is when we don't pause for a moment and think more deeply about the thought we've just had. Instead, we allow ourselves to believe it and then act upon it, either mentally or physically. What's more, these kinds of negative thoughts can pop into our heads without invitation, leading to a negative mindset and low moods at random times. The result of this is that we become stuck in a loop of negativity that repeats over and over again.

The solution to disrupting this loop is to become aware of the way we talk to ourselves. A neural pathway is formed when we train our brain to do something for the first time, and after a while, it becomes a learned behaviour that we carry out as second nature. This is because our brains are developing and learning all the time, so we can create new, positive pathways instead of continuing to trudge down the old ones.

When we first learn the new way of behaving, it's as if we're walking through a field of tall grass. It can sometimes be tricky to navigate and we might find ourselves getting lost or going off course. As we carry out the same behaviour over and over again, the grass is flattened and a track slowly starts to form in our brain. Over time, we tread it so often it becomes the only one we walk down; we don't even need to think about it.

These neural pathways apply to our drinking; we've done it for years, so it's automatic. The good news is that if we become mindful we can change the way we think, and create pathways that lead to new and positive destinations. What's more, once this happens the grass starts to grow over the old ones and they soon become unused and forgotten.

What all this is pointing to is the fact that you don't have to listen to your personal negativity or 'inner critic'; you can silence them altogether simply by becoming aware of them and choosing not to act on what you hear.

Below are the most common negative thoughts along with examples of how you might be acting on them. Each thought type is accompanied by an example of a more positive way to act, which is sure to help you achieve a long-term positive frame of mind.

Thought type: Thinking all the time

This means: Your mind produces negative thoughts constantly and you use words, like always, never, why, everyone, or everything.

Example of what you might say to yourself: It always happens to me, why does everything go wrong?

How to change your thinking: You have the power to change anything. Each day offers a new opportunity and a chance for a fresh start.

Thought type: Black and white thinking

This means: Everything is either good or bad with no in-between.

Example of what you might say to yourself: I slipped up and drank, everything is ruined.

How to change your thinking: We know this isn't true. You made a mistake and you're upset because it matters to you; learn from it and do better tomorrow.

Thought type: Believing what you're thinking

This means: You rely on what your feelings tell you and act on them without seeking proof.

Example of what you might say to yourself: I feel like my life will be boring if I stop drinking.

How to change your thinking: You don't know this – you haven't tried life without drinking long-term so you have no evidence. Life wasn't boring when you were young but you didn't drink then.

Thought type: Negative thoughts/filtering

This means: You always see the negative and filter out the positive, even though the positive is there.

Example of what you might say to yourself: I made a mistake at work. I've ruined everything and may as well quit and find a new job before I get fired.

How to change your thinking: You made a mistake today, but you've also had five years in the job when you didn't make a mistake and your employer values you. Everyone makes mistakes and you now have extra motivation to be even better at work.

Thought type: Thoughts of guilt and regret

This means: You allow thoughts of guilt or regret to control your behaviour and use words like 'should have', 'have to', and 'must'.

Example of what you might say to yourself: I should have gone to the gym today, but I didn't. I will never get fit.

How to change your thinking: So what, you can go tomorrow and you know you don't need to hit the gym every day to get fit. This is an opportunity to make a training programme and stick to it.

Thought type: Catastrophic thinking

This means: You always think something awful or disastrous is going to happen.

Example of what you might say to yourself: What if I didn't turn off the oven? My house will burn down.

How to change your thinking: How many of your past catastrophic thoughts turned into reality? None of them. Stay rational and learn to calm your mind and thoughts.

Thought type: Predicting the future

This means: You anticipate the outcome before it's even happened.

Example of what you might say to yourself: I have drunk alcohol for so long, I'll never be able to change.

How to change your thinking: These negative thoughts can be self-fulfilling. Use them as an opportunity to make a change and know that you're probably wrong about your future predictions.

'I don't know about anyone else but the constant reprimanding hasn't subsided! The negative self-talk is so loud at the moment! Going to be really gentle with myself today. The underlying emotion of it is fear. I'm fearful of not fitting in, not losing weight, not being accepted. I'm hoping that if I'm not suppressing these emotions with drink they will soon go away.'
Facebook group post by NH, Bedfordshire, UK

'I want to share something very valuable about the importance of HOW you talk to yourself when you want to achieve something like sobriety.
Do you know that your subconscious ignores the word 'NOT'?
Try this:
Think about chocolate.
What are you thinking about?
Yes, chocolate.
Now, don't think about chocolate.
What are you thinking about?
Yes, chocolate (mostly).
So it's very important to AVOID using the word 'not' when consciously telling yourself what you want to do.
Avoid saying 'I WON'T drink tonight'. Instead, say 'I WILL stay sober tonight.'
It really works! If you're not convinced, try it the first way and listen to what your wine witch says to you – I bet she says 'go on, have a drink' rather than 'don't stay sober'. She knows the power of positive language. We need to as well, to fight her effectively.
Good luck, stay sober, enjoy all the benefits.'
Facebook group post by AB, Bedfordshire, UK

Chapter 24
Help! I'm going to an event and I won't be able to drink

'I can only enjoy a party if I have a drink.'

In my drinking days, if I had an event coming up (such as a wedding or a party), the first thing I'd think about was alcohol. I'd check what time it started and then plan exactly when I'd have my first tipple and what it would be. I liked to have a drinking strategy, and for me, the entire event would revolve around alcohol – although the reality was that as soon as I arrived, I'd get stuck into the free champagne or whatever else was available, regardless of what I'd planned. Then, once I'd started I wouldn't stop. Even after the bar had closed and the music and dancing had finished, I'd tuck into my own supply of red wine because I thought stopping drinking at 1:00am would spoil the 'fun' I was entitled to have.

It was the same with any special occasion: weddings, parties, family get-togethers, and even funerals. The drink was always in charge. This often resulted in regrettable and embarrassing behaviour (which I often couldn't even remember), made worse by the fact that it was carried out in front of my friends and loved ones. At the time, it seemed funny, but when I woke the next morning with a dull throb in my head and was reminded about what I'd done the night before, it was no longer something to laugh about. At this point, it was a case of trying to repair the damage, which was incredibly difficult when I felt like death and just wanted to sleep off the hangover.

I recently realised that an excellent test to discover whether you're truly liberated from alcohol or still fixated with it is to ask yourself which of the following statements are true for you if you're going to a party.

A) As you approach the door you're thinking about where your first drink will come from, what it will be, and how soon you can get your hands on it. No sooner do you have it than you're starting to think about the next one.

B) As you approach the door, instead of thinking about alcohol, you're thinking about the friends inside, what the conversation will be like, and how the event will go. You might also imagine the food, dancing, and the new people you'll meet.

You won't be surprised to hear that the first statement used to be true for me. Wherever I went, booze came first, and I always made sure I had it in plentiful supply – even if it meant stashing the plastic insides of a wine box down my trousers (which was my tactic when I went to music festivals that didn't allow alcohol). But since I've quit drinking, the second statement now holds true for me, and I've discovered that events and special occasions are so much more fun without it involved. When I go to any of them now, I'm fully present and engaged, and find myself wrapped up in conversation and laughter like never before. Without the alcohol obsession, I'm simply free to enjoy myself and go with the flow.

It wasn't easy at the start

The first few events I went to after I quit drinking felt like a challenge; I was still early in my journey and felt fragile. It was scary to think I might be tempted or pressured by people, and cave in just to please them. I recall the company Christmas party a few months after I'd quit. There was no getting out of it as I owned the firm and had to be there – I wasn't going to let people down. The staff all love the annual knees-up, which takes place at a fancy hotel with hundreds of people from other businesses in a glitzy ballroom.

Champagne is served from 7:00pm, and the drinking and dancing go on into the early hours. There's a free bar all night long.

As the party approached, I decided I needed to plan ahead; if I turned up without a strategy it could end in disaster. So that's exactly what I did, and I want to share this with you so that you can use this same kind of planning tactic for yourself.

I called the hotel and asked them what alcohol-free drinks were available. They had a few things I liked, but I also asked if I was able to bring my own drinks and stash them under the table. They said it wasn't a problem. I now knew exactly what I'd be drinking – it wasn't open to any kind of debate, the decision was made. I also decided I would drive, as this gave me both the power to leave when I wanted and a non-negotiable reason why I couldn't drink (I knew I would never drink and drive).

I also made myself accountable by talking to some of my closest colleagues in the company. I explained that I no longer drank and wouldn't be drinking at the party; they were incredibly supportive, and when the big night came they all had my back and looked out for me. This also resulted in one of them opening up to me about how she was worried about her own drinking.

Part of my planning had been to think about who I was going to surround myself with. I was able to choose who I sat next to, which was helpful because the last thing I wanted was to be beside a heavy boozer or someone who would encourage me to drink. I appreciate this option isn't always available, but there's no harm in asking.

I also visualised how it would go. We covered this earlier in the book, but this strategy is amazing so it's worth repeating it here. I spent some time with my eyes closed and pictured myself pulling up and parking in the car park. I could see what I was wearing, and imagined myself walking to the venue and meeting my colleagues in the foyer where the Champagne reception would be held. I played through the conversations, during which people said, 'Why aren't you having Champagne?' so that when it happened for real I'd be prepared. It was important to make the visualisation as detailed as possible so I could put myself there in the moment. If you try this, it's worth writing it down before you go and then comparing it to the reality after the event.

When the night of the Christmas party finally came around, I had a great time, the food was lovely, and I had plenty of laughs and great conversations. I even ended up on the dance floor. I did feel rather self-conscious dancing while sober at first, but then I realised most people were drunk and couldn't care less about what I was doing. Even if they did care, I doubted whether they would remember. The first time you dance without drinking is an amazingly liberating feeling; I remember smiling as I bopped away and thinking to myself, 'This is it! I'm dancing sober and enjoying it. I'm actually free now.'

On the downside, I also learned that after a few hours at boozy events, most people tend to be well on the way to being drunk. They end up repeating themselves, slurring words, not listening, and can be annoying (to think I used to be like that). You may find you just don't want to be there when people start to get like this, and that's totally fine. So when it came to midnight I decided it was time to leave, say my goodbyes, and drive myself home. The joy of waking up the next morning with no hangover was amazing – I went for a long walk in the woods and appreciated being happy and alive.

Later in the day, I couldn't avoid having a little smile to myself when I saw the pictures my drunk colleagues had posted on Facebook from the night before. I was so glad to be free of the stupid behaviour that I'd used to think was funny and cool. There were also a couple of 'hangover' pictures that made me feel extremely grateful for the clear head I was enjoying.

So that was how I made it through my first Christmas party, but it was almost twelve months without drinking before I received an invite to my first wedding. Even though I was much stronger by this stage, I still used the same tactics as there was no way I was going to let myself get caught out. It played out in pretty much the same way as the Christmas party – I had a great time dancing and joining in the fun. One thing I did notice, though, was that quite a few people weren't drinking. I'd always assumed everyone drank like I used to, but clearly, my haze of red wine had deluded me and I'd used this belief as a way of justifying my own habit.

Just like at the Christmas party, by midnight it was mainly the drunk people who were left and I headed home with a clear head and some wonderful memories of an amazing day. That's another thing I've discovered: when you don't drink at events, you get to keep the memories forever.

Of course, special occasions don't always involve other people. There will also be times when you want to celebrate on your own or with your family, such as on a wedding anniversary, birthday, or even on reaching one of your sober milestones (being sober means you now have two birthdays). Below are a few suggestions for celebrating without alcohol involved, whatever the situation:

Book a spa day. Relax either on your own or with friends; this is one of my favourite ways to celebrate something.

Go for a special meal. Book your favourite restaurant or try a new one; you're now saving calories and cash, so you can afford to spend a bit more on your meal.

Take a holiday or short break. It could be somewhere close to home or a far-flung destination; either is a wonderful way to celebrate.

Eat some sweet treats. These aren't just for children! Cakes, ice-cream, and sweets are a great way to treat yourself.

Enjoy a day out. It could be a trip to the zoo, an amusement park, or a museum; your choices are almost endless.

Do nothing. If you lead a hectic life and feel like you never have time to yourself, maybe doing absolutely nothing for a day is just the kind of celebration you need.

'Went to a friend's birthday party tonight. I was the only person aside from the kids not drinking. They were doing shots and all sorts of drinks were flowing – including a bottle of my old favourite wine. I did not want to drink. I had no desire. I did not know many people, so that was tough for me and made me somewhat anxious. I stayed for over two hours – which was a bit of a struggle.

I did it. I am proud of me. I was able to bring my daughter and her friend home with me and there was no danger of driving while drunk.

Some things I learned tonight:
It is okay to leave when you want.
You don't need to stay and watch people get drunk.
You may need to find new people to spend time with – or different ways to spend time with them.
Being sober is so much better than being drunk!!
Stay strong my sober friends!!! We've got this!'
Facebook group post by DB, Georgia, USA

'45 days alcohol-free today after over 30 years of drinking daily. I overcame a huge test yesterday when I attended a fabulous wedding. The first dry wedding of my adult life. I laughed, danced and had an all-round brilliant time. I woke up nice and early this morning, hangover free and looking forward to a walk in the

Cumbrian hills, followed by more celebrations this afternoon.
Haven't felt this good in ages. #nevergoingback'
Facebook group post by SB, Leeds, UK

Chapter 25
I'm not losing weight yet

'Will I ever lose the extra pounds?'

You may have heard about people losing loads of weight when they quit drinking, and you're asking yourself, why hasn't this happened to me yet? But stop and think for a moment. You didn't go alcohol-free just to lose weight, did you? I'm pretty sure you see it as an added bonus of the sober lifestyle you've chosen, rather than the main aim.

What's the real reason you want to stop drinking?

With this in mind, have you thought about the reasons you don't want alcohol in your life? If not, it's worth exploring them now (or reminding yourself of them if you worked them out at the beginning). Why are you on this journey? Why are you reading this book? Why do you want to change?

Here are some of the answers I wrote down when I did this exercise before I quit drinking.

- I'm fed up of alcohol controlling my life; I hate thinking about drinking all the time and it being in charge of almost everything I do.
- I've had enough of hangovers, fuzzy heads, and not having energy or motivation because I've been drinking the night before.
- My anxiety is terrible and I've read that quitting alcohol might help.

- I hate the fact that I often put my drinking ahead of spending quality time with my teenage daughter; she should come first.
- I'm worried about the long-term health impact of my daily drinking, and am scared I'll be dead before I reach 50.

A great exercise to do after you've made your list is to explore each answer in depth. You should also write an 'opposite' statement next to each answer and see if the new 'opposite' statement could be true for you.

For example, my first answer was:

'I'm fed up of alcohol controlling my life. I hate thinking about drinking all the time and it being in charge of almost everything I do.'

An opposite statement that was true for me:

'If alcohol wasn't in my life, there's a good chance I wouldn't be thinking about it all the time, and it wouldn't have control over the things I do. I would like to see how this feels for me and if it holds true.'

It's important you believe the 'opposite' statement to be true – make sure it's something you wholeheartedly stand by. This is why I stated there was a 'good chance' and 'I would like to see how this feels for me'. Because in this case, I couldn't say for an absolute fact whether it was true until I'd experienced it for real. Make your statement honest. By doing so you'll see what your life could be like without alcohol in it; you'll also take a close look at what you believe about sobriety and alcohol, and how correct your statements really are.

The relationship between weight and alcohol

Okay, so maybe losing weight is one of the reasons you're on this journey. Let's talk a little about weight loss and alcohol.

It's a fact that alcoholic drinks contain a huge amount of calories. A pint of beer has around 200 and a 750ml bottle of wine around 600. So over an average week of drinking, I was consuming at least 6,000 calories – that's almost a third of a million a year! Take a minute to calculate your annual alcoholic drink calorie intake – it can be an eye-opener.

There are conflicting studies about how much alcohol consumption impacts on weight gain, but all reports agree to one degree or another that it definitely causes it to some extent. Put simply, the more often and heavily you drink, the more weight you'll likely gain. Another study concluded that drinking alcohol either before or during meals can increase your intake of calories through the course of the meal, and recommended avoiding alcoholic drinks with food altogether. Of course, if your judgement is clouded from alcohol there's also every chance you'll find yourself eating more; we've all experienced those midnight burgers and kebabs on the way home after a night of drinking. Obviously, I recommend avoiding alcoholic drinks at all times, but it's interesting that the study showed mealtimes to somehow boost the calorific properties of alcohol.

The obvious fact is that if we cut alcohol out of our lives we're going to eliminate a lot of calories. When combined with a healthy diet and lifestyle, we're set for success when it comes to staying in good shape, and I've spoken to hundreds of people who've quit drinking and almost all of them have lost weight.

But here's the thing: it can take time, and it's rarely a straight, downwards line when you stand on the scales. Please read that twice. It's important to remember this so you don't lose heart after a month of not drinking and possibly finding yourself slightly heavier.

One added element that can mess with your weight when you cut alcohol out of your life is that if you're like many people, you might turn to sugary snacks and soda drinks to replace the booze. This can mean your weight stays the same, or you could even add on a few pounds in the short term. Don't worry about it, because losing weight wasn't why you quit in the first place.

A couple of months after I stopped drinking I had much more energy and motivation to do things. I got back into running, joined a fitness bootcamp, and found myself taking regular walks in nature. Despite that, it still took four to six months of sobriety before I lost weight because my body needed time to adjust. I've found the same story holds true with most people I speak to.

So stick with it and don't beat yourself up if you don't turn into a size six super-model two weeks after throwing your Chablis bottles away, because there's so much more to gain from a sober life than weight loss alone. For me, gaining happiness and a sense of peace and calm in my life were far more important. It's best to view losing weight as another gift of sobriety; when you cut such a large number of calories out of your life, the chances are you'll see a measurable difference over the course of time. Just don't expect instant results.

It's worth taking a full body photo at the start of your alcohol-free journey and then comparing it to one taken after a couple of months without drinking. Continue to do this at regular intervals, as it will help you stay focused and give you a visual reminder of the rewards of sobriety.

'Working out... this time last year I was 11st 8lbs, battling my weight and getting off the booze.
Now I'm 9st 1lb.

Alcohol-free for 5 months.
Loving my new sober life.'
Facebook group post by HT, Nottingham, UK

'I'm so excited, and I just can't hide it.
I spent some of my sober savings on new jeans. I've waited 100 days
and FINALLY, I'm losing a little weight, so I got into a size 14 for the
first time in several years.
I can't breathe, let alone eat, but never mind!'
Facebook group post by AB, Bedfordshire, UK

'Hi all... here is what's going on with me and I would relish your
thoughts, experiences and input. I am on day 85. I am 59 years old.
Not only have I not lost weight, but I've picked up about 8 lbs. I feel
like I am going in the wrong direction.

I am learning about a Keto diet/lifestyle, have given up about 98%
sugar and caffeine and 100% gluten, pasta, bread etc. If I have
chocolate, it's the 80-95% cocoa dark chocolate. I do try to walk
with my dog every day, anywhere from 1.5 – 3 miles. I also work
full-time and am on my feet the entire time. My sober app says that
it takes about 4 months for an alcohol-free person to begin to see
changes in their weight.

For my own self-analysis, I still think that I am eating too many
calories. And, while I do not need to reward myself as much now as
when I first started this string of alcohol-free days, I do indulge in an
Iced-Cloud Caramel Macchiato, and ice cream every once in a while,
but not every day. While this all may seem a tad self-indulgent – and
I am trying not to worry too much about this – I would like to lose a
little bit of weight on this healthy journey!
Anyway, hope I don't sound like I'm whining. That wasn't my intent.
Just looking to see if anyone can relate, or anything else you want to
add. Happy Sober Sunday, ya'll!
P.S. Sober living is the best! Sending lots of sober and encouraging
hugs to everyone!'

Facebook group post by MF, Little River, SC, USA

Chapter 26
Will I be boring without alcohol?

'I'm worried no-one will want to know me if I'm always sober.'

When I cast my mind back to my red wine days, I always used to think people who didn't drink were boring losers who were missing out. I'd even make sarcastic comments about why they weren't joining in with the 'fun'. For instance, there were a couple of younger guys in my company in their early 20s who didn't drink and never had done. I remember giving them a hard time about it at our company Christmas party because I thought they were spoiling the spirit of the occasion. It wasn't that they didn't dance all night and have a great time – it was that I assumed that they couldn't be having *real* fun without drinking.

Of course, I now know this to be totally wrong: we have the best fun when we're sober. As time went by, I started to wonder if those guys were onto something…

When I finally found the power to quit drinking, I was so excited and happy about the wonderful changes I was experiencing that I couldn't help myself from shouting it from the rooftops. I plastered my joy about my new-found sobriety all over my social media accounts, and thought everyone would jump at the chance to support me. Most people were great, but a couple of close friends surprised me with their reactions. One even called me 'boring' (ouch!). I just couldn't get over being called boring – I'd always been the life and soul of the party and didn't see why anything needed to change just because I no longer chose to drink.

After I'd recovered from the shock, I tried to think about why someone would say something like that. I bet if I'd announced I'd quit smoking or taking drugs I wouldn't have had that reaction. It didn't take me long to realise that for some people, my talking about quitting drinking held up a mirror to their own relationship with alcohol, and I don't imagine they liked what was staring back at them. They might also have felt that I was judging them for it (not that I was). In addition, I wonder if they thought they were losing a drinking buddy and friend. My relationships with the people who made those comments were mainly based around boozy nights out, so I could understand why they would think this.

The reality was that after more than two decades of drinking a bottle or more of red wine every day, I'd found the whole routine of hangovers, cravings, anxiety, regretful behaviour, and worrying about my health starting to become very boring indeed. I hadn't given any thought as to whether people would think I was poor company when I quit drinking; I just felt excited about what was ahead of me.

These days my life is happy, peaceful, and much calmer than in the drinking days. Granted, I don't go out getting smashed, but is my life boring now? No, it's anything but. Since I quit alcohol I've experienced new levels of motivation and energy, found new friends, and got involved in extra hobbies and projects. In fact, I feel like I never stop, and always have interesting and fun things to do.

I've also had amazing opportunities appear in my life that have only come to me through quitting drinking. I've written this book, been invited to speak at live events, and have worked with hundreds of inspirational people from around the world. None of this would have happened if I hadn't put down the bottle. There have also been several holidays, and they've all been brilliant – no hunting for wine shops five minutes after arriving. It feels so good to experience everything while being fully present, and to have clear memories of my trips that I can keep forever. I find myself laughing more, my anxiety has gone, and I'm genuinely happier. How can that be boring?

So I guess when people call us sober warriors boring, it comes from a place of not knowing what's on the other side. Okay, we don't have the war stories to share the next morning of how we ended up in jail, passed out in a bush, wet the bed, or had unprotected sex with someone whose name we can't remember. But is that really fun? Of course, it isn't.

Assuming you agree this isn't a true picture of what a good time looks like, then what's the fun part when you're drinking? Sure, the first drink makes us feel a little euphoric and tipsy, and we giggle and laugh more which can feel nice. But as we quaff more and more drinks, our brain releases downer chemicals to rebalance the huge rush of happy chemicals it's already pumped out. So we often end up feeling sad, edgy, and low by the end of the evening. This feeling is what can lead to aggression and teary meltdowns.

I've been to gigs, festivals, parties, and celebrations sober, and I've had far more fun than when I was drinking. Without alcohol in my life, I've found enjoyment and happiness in so many new things – activities that I probably wouldn't have got involved with as a drinker. I (and my life) am anything but boring.

Now here's one thing that turns the concept of a non-drinker being called 'boring' on its head… I've realised it's the drunk people who are the boring ones. When I've been at events at which most people are drinking, I've found that after a few hours most people have had too much to drink. When they talk, the following happens:

- they talk loudly, slur and repeat themselves;
- they don't listen to what you're saying;
- they repeat themselves – again;

- then they talk even louder and continue to slur and repeat what they've already said, and
- they spray you with spit when they talk.

Believe me, it gets really, really boring. I often find that by midnight I've had my fun and leave the drinkers to carry on their journey to alcohol oblivion, while I drive home to my comfy bed in the knowledge that I won't have a raging hangover the next day.

The truth is, some of the most interesting, colourful, and crazy people I know are sober, and some of the most boring people I know are heavy drinkers. Maybe some non-drinkers are a little boring, or just introverts, and if they are then good for them – that's totally fine. There's no point drinking and turning yourself into an extrovert if that isn't who you are. When you're sober you're free to be yourself, and as long as you're happy, it doesn't matter.

As a footnote to this chapter, a few months ago, one of the friends who made some of those negative comments told me that she was concerned about how much she was drinking. I gave her the tools and support she needed, and helped her to explore her relationship with alcohol. At the time of writing, she hasn't had an alcoholic drink for four months, and has told me she has no plans to return to drinking as her life has improved in so many ways. She hasn't said anything about her life now being 'boring'.

'Hi Be Sober gang. I haven't contributed to the page in a while so I thought I'd just check-in. I'm just about 250 days sober and there is much which is different about my sober life now. At about 3 months in, I realised that I'd simply lost the desire to drink. That situation is still the same. I regard myself as very fortunate, but I can be around alcohol in any situation now and I'm totally unfazed. Not only do I not think about alcohol anymore, I actually seldom think about sobriety either. That's partly why I'm much less active within sobriety groups now. I've had a great year so far and life is good. I've become involved in new interests, met some great people

through those new interests and learned that there's a whole life out there to be lived without everything revolving around booze! Thanks to all those of you who have helped me get to this place.'
Facebook post by KR, UK

Chapter 27
I feel lonely and bored
without alcohol

'I use alcohol to fill the emptiness in my life; letting go scares me.'

Having a partner or close family around us when we quit drinking provides valuable support and accountability. But we don't all have this luxury, and even if we do it's important that we're well prepared for how to deal with any feelings of loneliness and boredom that may arise as we travel along the path to sobriety.

It is clear from the people I encounter in the groups I work with, the main reason they feel lonely is because they don't have a partner or someone significant to spend quality time with. This isolation can lead them to think about drinking as a way of blotting out the discomfort, but please believe me when I say that you're far better off facing up to these feelings than reaching for a drink.

Some people also feel lonely when they find they have had to walk away from the friends that came with their drinking. As we grow into new people, we can become less interested in the activities and people who we previously thought brought us pleasure, and I've seen friendships drift apart as a result of people wanting different things in life.

Quitting drinking frees up a significant amount of time in our lives. Have you ever calculated the time you spend (or spent) drinking alcohol? If not, take a moment to work it out and write it in your journal. For me, it was 20 to 25 hours a week. When I cut it out, that amounted to a serious amount of extra time on my hands and yes, on occasion, this led to me feeling slightly bored and a little lonely.

There's nothing wrong with feeling like this at times. In fact, some people crave a life of solitude and love spending time in their own headspace. However, we humans are social creatures and it's important to have the right balance in your life. You certainly wouldn't want feelings of loneliness expanding into thoughts about drinking. It's far better to do something proactive, and in this chapter, I'll share my tips to help you combat this issue.

Ways of dealing with loneliness and boredom

Find new groups or interests. The first thing I did was to join a fitness bootcamp, and this led to me making some great new friends. It felt good to have relationships that weren't based around drinking – they felt so much more honest and authentic without alcohol involved. Think about the activities you like to do and start searching for clubs or groups in your area.

Make a sober bucket list. Write down all the achievements you'd like to make in your alcohol-free life, and get to work on ticking them off the list. They don't have to be huge challenges (although I'd include a few significant ones to aim for), because on this journey, even small goals feel like big wins. You might think about far-away destinations you want to travel to, that art or yoga class you never got round to joining, or it could be something more adventurous, like skydiving or rock climbing. The sky really is the limit and you can make your bucket list as long and detailed as you wish.

Practice gratitude. I mentioned this earlier as a way of coping with blue days, but it works equally well for combating feelings of loneliness or boredom. Every day, write down three to five things you feel grateful for. It could be something simple, like right now I'm feeling grateful for a lovely view from my office window of the fields and the horses lying in the sun, so I'm going to put that in my journal today. Try and do this every single day to remind yourself of the wonderful things in your life.

Check out 'meet-up' websites. These are dedicated to meet-ups for people who like different activities. You'll find everything from groups for book enthusiasts, through to art and roller-skating. Take a look – you'll very likely discover one that captures your interest and imagination.

Care for others. It might seem counter-intuitive, but looking out for the lives of others will ensure that you remain focused on taking care of your own. You could get a pet, or even just a plant to take care of. In my first few months sober, I found a local charity and spent time visiting people who were unable to leave their homes by themselves. It was immensely rewarding to visit them for a chat and a cup of tea, and I know they genuinely appreciated having someone to talk to.

You'll have so much more energy and motivation to do things when you quit drinking that you'll want to get out and about and involve yourself in new activities. When I first stopped, I wondered what I would do with all the extra time on my hands, yet now I struggle to fit things into my hectic schedule. How I managed to find 20 to 25 hours a week for drinking I'll never know!

However, I did have to be proactive. If I'd sat around waiting for new friends and activities to drop into my lap, it may never have happened. So make sure you take the first steps and you'll soon find any feelings of loneliness or boredom fading away. Above all, be patient. It can take time to discover the 'new you' and the person you're becoming, but I can assure you that you're going to be the very best version of yourself that you've ever been as you go on this incredible journey.

'I feel so bloody lonely. I chase for scraps of time with my children, but teenagers aren't really interested in a mum with a drink problem unless there's something in it for them really. My husband kicked me out into a nasty housing association flat last year after 30 years of marriage and my life has been a waking nightmare ever since. I knew our marriage had problems, and the alcohol was both the problem and the solution for me. He announced to anyone who would listen that I was gone, even leaving me some of the things I needed from my old home under a bush nearby so he didn't have to actually see me. Anyway, I have a father I speak to sometimes but no other family or friends, and trying to stay sober when all I really want to do is find the courage to check out and stop pretending I'm OK when I'm really not. I'm on day two again.'

Facebook group post by MA, Rochester, UK

Chapter 28
I can't sleep without a drink

'Alcohol helps me sleep; if I don't drink I'll be awake all night.'

I firmly used to believe that I needed alcohol in order to help me sleep. I was convinced that if I didn't have a drink before bedtime, I wouldn't be relaxed and calm, and my mind would be racing as soon as I shut my eyes. This was a daily habit, which created yet another excuse to justify my drinking. If I didn't drink I wouldn't sleep, so of course, I needed more wine!

I find it hard to switch my buzzing brain off even in the most relaxing of situations, so I was incredibly worried about what would happen to my sleeping patterns when I quit alcohol. I know sleep is something you may be concerned about too, so this chapter is designed to help.

The truth about alcohol and sleep

What I didn't understand when I was drinking was that I was never getting a refreshing night's sleep in any case. With alcohol in my system, my entire sleep cycle had become disrupted. I was spending more time awake than if I hadn't drunk and was having fewer dreams. I also had an elevated heart rate.

This is because *without* alcohol in our bloodstream we move in cycles between deep sleep (when our bodies are in 'healing' mode) and Rapid Eye Movement (REM) sleep (when our brains reset and refresh themselves, ready for the next day). Dreamy REM sleep is important because it stimulates the areas of the brain that we use to learn and develop. It's also associated with the production of proteins in our bodies. Without REM sleep we can feel sluggish, and over time our mental sharpness can be impacted negatively.

This explains why, after drinking, I used to feel unmotivated and would struggle to get going each day. Even though I thought I was enjoying a proper night of refreshing sleep, it was not the case because I was never having the REM sleep that my body and mind so desperately needed. I didn't realise any of this was going on; I just carried on in blissful unawareness, assuming that the sluggish feelings were part of the daily hangover I had to endure from drinking wine the night before. But it was so much more than that – no wonder I had huge, dark shadows underneath my eyes.

I remember the first day I didn't drink. That evening I went to bed as normal without a drop of alcohol in my body. I tossed and turned in bed for hours, my mind racing, and had a rough night of broken sleep. In the morning, I felt more tired than when I'd gone to bed, which brought back memories of how exhausted I had been when my daughter was a baby and she would wake in the night wanting a feed or her nappy changed. Of course, this terrible night convinced me I needed alcohol in order to sleep, so I went straight back to drinking and woke up believing that my sleep problem was resolved. It may have been resolved in my mind, but that was far from the truth and I also still had a serious drinking problem to contend with.

I wanted to succeed in sobriety, but the struggle with sleep was tough. I decided to go back to the drawing board and research everything I could about the facts relating to alcohol and sleeping. I knew this was going to be an obstacle I had to overcome if I wanted to move forward in a positive direction. Once I had the knowledge, I had the power and now knew what I was doing to my body and mind.

It was clear to me that I was never going to recover if I wasn't allowing myself proper sleep and the opportunity to heal, which would entail riding out a few difficult nights. I saw it as short-term pain for long-term gain. So after a few more failed attempts to get past more than one day without drinking, I tried again with a new feeling of strength, hope, and determination to succeed.

The daytime felt fairly easy as I was never a big daytime drinker. It was the evenings that were harder as that was when wine o'clock would always come around. Then it came to bedtime. I want to be totally honest with you here so that you know what to expect: for the first few nights I was constantly tossing and turning, my sleep was broken, and I found it almost impossible to silence my buzzing brain so that I could fall asleep.

I'm not alone in this. Members of my groups have told me they've experienced sweating and hot flushes in the night, and I think almost every ex-drinker experiences vivid dreams as their brains recalibrate to normal sleep patterns. The worst dreams are the ones from which you wake up convinced you've just had an alcoholic drink. This has happened to me on more than one occasion.

The rough period of broken sleep lasted just over a week. Then, one day I woke up and realised I'd just experienced the best night of sleep I could remember in years. It felt amazing. I felt refreshed, energised, motivated, and truly alive. If this was what one night of proper, refreshing sleep felt like, I wondered what I would experience after a month or more. After that first night, I was actually excited about going to bed the next day and couldn't wait to experience it again. My mind was no longer racing when I lay down, and a few minutes after my head hit the pillow I was heading off to a land of sweet slumber. It's been that way ever since.

After a few weeks of this beautiful new pattern of sleep, I took a photo of myself and compared it to one from when I'd been drinking. I was amazed to see that the darkness under my eyes that I'd carried around with me for years had almost totally vanished. I took this as a sign that my body was healing and I was moving in the right direction.

So don't expect instant wonderful sleep on the first day you stop drinking – you need to give it time. However, you can use some of my tactics below to set you up for success when it comes to achieving relaxing and refreshing sleep.

Be comfortable. It sounds obvious but make sure your mattress, pillow, and bedding are all as comfortable as they can be. It can be easy to hold on to the same bed long after it's past its life expectancy, but that's not going to help you achieve the level of comfort and sleep you deserve.

Unwind. Your mind and body need to move into sleep mode before you go to bed. Try to avoid using electronic devices in the hour before you retire, as the light they emit has been proven to stimulate your brain and make it hard for you to switch off. Reading or practising relaxation techniques, such as meditation, are great ways to prepare for bedtime.

Avoid naps. It makes sense that you want to be tired when you go to bed at night. If you've been napping during the day there's a much higher chance that you'll struggle to get to sleep.

Exercise. I know from personal experience that when I exercise I always get off to sleep quickly. The more vigorous the exercise, the more tired I am and the better I seem to sleep. Try to ensure that you take regular exercise to help your own sleep.

Keep to a schedule. Try to stick to roughly the same schedule each day. I go to bed between 10:00pm and 11:00pm each night, which keeps my body and mind in the same routine, and the more I've stuck to this the easier sleeping has become.

Most people find it only takes around a week or two to start experiencing deep and refreshing sleep, so stick with your non-drinking routine and you'll get there before long. Plus, you can use these tactics to help. Once you experience that first night of incredible sleep, you'll never look back.

'I dreamed last night that I had 200 days sober, but didn't think about it until AFTER I'd shared a bottle of red wine with an ex?! Nooooo – It was horrible! I was so relieved when I woke up in the middle of the night to realise that it was a bad dream.'
Facebook group post by EO, Switzerland

Chapter 29
How can I have sex without drinking?

'I can't imagine sex without a drink; I wouldn't be able to relax and enjoy it.'

If you're like many people you may be using alcohol to loosen up and feel relaxed when it comes to sex. This can be a real barrier when it comes to quitting drinking, as it can be easy to assume your sex life will end at the same time as your alcohol habit. Please don't worry, because this isn't the case. In fact, the opposite is true: without alcohol involved, you can experience the best sex and a level of intimacy that you may never have enjoyed before.

How alcohol affects your sex life

- Alcohol is proven to lower inhibitions; this can make it easy to end up sleeping with someone you don't really know, love, or trust (which can lead to feelings of regret and low self-esteem).
- With lowered inhibitions comes the increased risk of STDs and unwanted pregnancy.
- When you're drunk your senses are dulled, so you don't feel the same level of physical sensation as when you're clear-headed.
- For men, alcohol is proven to be a cause of erectile dysfunction. There are numerous documented cases of men being unable to sustain an erection after drinking, and drinking heavily over time can make what might otherwise

have been the odd episode of 'brewers' droop' a regular problem.

- For women, alcohol can cause problems with lubrication and reduce the ability to reach orgasm; even if orgasm is reached, the intensity can be severely impacted.
- Alcohol can cause fertility and menstrual problems, making it harder to become pregnant.
- Alcohol lowers your self-confidence; with drink involved you aren't truly empowered to seek what you want in the bedroom, or be fully in control of what you want to do.

I hope it's becoming clear now that alcohol does not improve sex. It lowers our inhibitions so it *feels* as if it's easier to get things moving, but the reality is that we don't experience the moment as it really is. We're not being the true version of ourselves, or doing justice to how sex should be experienced.

In the first weeks after I quit drinking, the realisation dawned on me that I would have to have sex without alcohol for the first time in over two decades. This scared me; I hadn't even thought about how sex might feature in my sober life. However, I reminded myself that sometimes the journey of self-growth meant I had to step outside my comfort zone. Yes, an easy option would have been to have a drink, reduce my inhibitions, and jump into bed, but that would have sent me right back down the rabbit hole with a bottle of wine in my hand. No thanks – my alcohol-free life came first, so this was just another area of my life I would need to explore.

The first thing I did was use my journal to explore my feelings and write down any concerns I had, and then to speak to my wife about how I felt. She was incredibly understanding and supportive, and we agreed to take things at a pace that worked for me. I felt a little like a 44-year-old virgin venturing into the world of sex for the first time. It was a strange experience, but also exciting and new.

When the time came I felt rather nervous and had quite a few 'what ifs' going on in my head. 'What if it only lasts five minutes?' 'What if it doesn't feel as good as when I used to drink?' But I knew this was part of the journey to being my true self, so I let the thoughts pass without judgement. I chose simply to experience sober sex for myself and to wait until afterwards before I decided how it felt.

I won't share the graphic details, but I will tell you that it was, without doubt, the best sex my wife and I had had together in years – an incredible experience. I felt sensations like never before, and it all seemed so much more vivid. It was a new experience to be fully present and in touch with my body (and hers), and to feel the pleasure without the numbing effect of alcohol. The wine-filled romps we used to have didn't touch it in terms of intensity. Yes, I was scared at first, but after that first time, there was no going back.

When I speak to people who are worried about sober sex, I find it's usually the thought of it that's scarier than the reality. So it makes sense to have a strategy to help ease your nerves and make you feel prepared. Use your journal to record your feelings and any concerns you have; you can also use the visualisation tactics I shared in previous chapters for when you go to an event sober, and then see how the real experience compares to your imagined scenario. I'm confident the reality will be way better than what you predict.

Here are my tips for sober sex

It sounds obvious but do it with someone you know, trust, and ideally, love. You're unlikely to do anything you regret with a stranger without alcohol involved, but it makes sense to ensure you share your intimacy with someone you care for and who cares for you.

Talk about it. Starting conversations about having sex without drink can seem daunting, but talking to your partner and ensuring you understand one another gives you transparency and the right approach in the bedroom. Discuss boundaries, needs, and what you expect, and don't forget to ask for what you want. This is probably the best thing that will ever happen to your sex life, and a great opportunity to rediscover a whole new world between the sheets.

Don't wait for your partner to make the first move. One of the toughest challenges can be wondering how to get things started. When you're drunk it seems to flow, but without drink involved, it can feel like an obstacle. I suggest talking about it first, then taking the first steps yourself. A great way to kick things off is to have a couples' bath or offer your partner a massage; ease yourself in gently and you'll soon find those worries vanishing as you become fully present in the moment.

Get to know your own body. Some people find that what they thought they enjoyed when drinking is no longer what they want to do when sober, so take the time to explore yourself and gain some clarity (you may want to do this on your own). By going through the process of quitting drinking, you'll have learned so much about self-acceptance that you can see this as just another step on the journey to achieving the life you want.

Enjoy it! You'll experience sensations and feelings that may be new to you, and it can be easy to become tense when exploring sex without the false protection of alcohol. Try and let go of any negative feelings and enjoy the moment – go with what feels good and savour the experience.

Don't feel embarrassed to reach out. If you're a member of an online sober group, don't assume you can't ask other members about sober sex. It's the perfect place to find non-judgemental support and advice if you have questions you don't feel comfortable discussing with your partner.

Yes, it can feel a little awkward first time around, but sober sex can give you a whole new level of intimacy and connection. For me, it's yet another gift the alcohol-free life has given, and once I had that first time out of the way, I knew I would never again want to experience sex any other way. That feeling of being totally present, engaged, and in touch with my senses was like nothing I had ever felt, so why would I want to numb myself with alcohol?

'You know you're sober when you don't need to ask your hubby if you had sex last night.'
Facebook post by EO, Switzerland

Chapter 30
After all this, I still want a drink

'I just can't let go of the idea that alcohol adds some kind of benefit to my life.'

You may have reached this chapter and feel like you've tried everything possible and *still* you have a desire to drink. If this is the case, don't despair – read on.

It took me multiple attempts to arrive at a place where I didn't want to drink any longer. For a long period, while I was trying to quit, half my mind was screaming at me to have a drink and telling me I deserved one, while the other half was saying I must stop and that I didn't need alcohol in my life. It was a pretty painful place to be, and dealing with this internal conflict was one of the biggest challenges I've faced. However, once I resolved it, I felt at peace. I made one decision to quit, put the bottle down, and have never looked back.

The key to ending my internal conflict was education combined with a change of mindset and positive action. It did mean stepping outside my comfort zone, but if I wanted to move in a positive direction, I had to do it. Below I've listed 10 actions I took (and you can take) to reach a point where I was free from alcohol, and no longer experiencing that painful back-and-forth in my mind.

10 ways to help you quit alcohol

1. Change your mindset. You need to change your beliefs about how alcohol benefits you. You want your thinking to shift from *can't have a drink* to *don't want one*. The way I did this was to educate myself by reading sober books, watching videos online, and connecting with other people on the same journey. The book *This Naked Mind* by Annie Grace was a game-changer for me and I would highly recommend reading it; by the end of it, there's a good chance you simply won't want to drink any longer.

2. Carry out an experiment. The first 30 days of being sober are the toughest, and the more you can stay focused the better. I signed up to the free 30-day Alcohol Experiment at www.thealcoholexperiment.com – this is an online programme that works with you day by day, virtually holding your hand. You're provided with daily video tutorials, an online journal, and a wealth of tools and help to engage you on your sober journey. Make sure you commit to it and take the time to check in every single day. Talking of tools, it's also worth downloading a sobriety counter app so you can count the days you've been alcohol-free; some people love the reward of reaching new milestones. That said, they don't work for everyone so see if they are right for you or not.

3. Take part in sober groups. Why not join a few Facebook sober groups? You'll find other people on the same journey who will give you support, inspiration, and encouragement. The *Be Sober* Facebook group is totally private which means nobody outside the group can see what you post. It's a fantastic place to find a caring community of sober warriors.

4. Find alternatives. Arm yourself with plenty of alcohol-free drinks. There are so many available and the market for botanical and alcohol-free drinks seems to be growing by the month. Part of the fun of a sober life is trying new options and discovering different flavours.

5. Throw it away. Pour away your alcoholic drinks – you don't want them in the house to tempt you. I dumped all my bottles of unopened red wine in a box at the end of my front garden with a sign that said, 'Free to a Good Home'. All 20 bottles were gone in under 15 minutes.

6. Avoid temptation. If you have any boozy nights out arranged in the first 30 days, I'd suggest avoiding them if you think you might be tempted to drink. After a month or two you'll be strong enough to attend just about any event (although drunken ones are generally boring), but in the early days, I consciously chose to steer clear of alcohol-based functions until I felt ready.

7. Enjoy the ride. Be passionate about what you're doing – this is such an incredible and positive change to your life, possibly one of the biggest you'll ever make. Try and approach the sober journey as if you've signed up to run a marathon (you can imagine the goal is initially to reach 100 days sober, for example, and each day is another training run). If you're torturing yourself by wishing you could drink each day you're going to struggle, but if you're excited by the fantastic new life that you're creating for yourself it's much easier. So get enthusiastic and be proud of yourself.

8. Learn from it. Don't worry if you slip up and have a drink – hardly anyone manages to quit drinking successfully at the very first attempt. Fall-backs happen with most of us so don't beat yourself up, just dust yourself down and get back on the sober journey, being that bit wiser and stronger from the experience. Make sure you use any lapses as an opportunity to learn; become curious about exactly what it was that made you drink. Explore how you felt and what triggered you so that you're better equipped next time.

9. Stay engaged. As the weeks and months roll past, you'll see so many wonderful and positive changes to your body, mind, and life that you'll probably never consider going back to drinking alcohol.

However, always be aware you could slip up, and stay on your guard. I find the best way to do this is to regularly take part in groups on Facebook and keep reading the books. I also find looking back at photos of how awful my skin looked and how bloated my face was to be a great way of reminding me how much better it is to be sober. In addition, writing down the reasons why I quit drinking in the first place has served as an excellent reminder to stay focused.

10. Keep busy. Find new things to do with the extra time you'll have. Use the opportunity to take up a new hobby; I like to go for a run, walk the dog, read, or go to the gym – think about what works for you. This helps to keep you away from alcohol. An added bonus is that being busy and active often results in you becoming fitter and healthier (unless your passion is baking cakes!).

And if you're still finding it hard…

If you're still struggling after you've read this book and worked through all the tips and advice, it may be worth considering one or more of the following options.

Find a one-to-one alcohol coach. Working one-to-one with a specialist can deliver outstanding results. It will also keep you incredibly engaged, motivated, and accountable.

Move from free support to paid. There are a number of paid groups and programmes that offer a much higher level of support than the free ones. They usually offer live interaction with an alcohol coach, often on a daily basis. This Naked Mind offers a range of programmes with daily engagement, question and answer sessions, and structured learning.

Seek medical help if you need it. Fewer than 10 percent of heavy drinkers are physically addicted to alcohol, which means, for the vast majority of people, achieving a sober life it's simply a matter of changing our beliefs and thinking. However, if you're struggling to change your mindset and free yourself from alcohol, despite trying everything, it may be worth you consulting your doctor.

Sober fears

When we start exploring what our life might look like without alcohol, it can feel scary, and there's no hiding from the fact that you have to face up to your worries. Below are 10 fears I had to deal with, along with the truth that was hiding behind them.

1. My life without alcohol will be boring. I now know that this idea couldn't be further from the truth. Since I stopped drinking, I've realised that if an event is boring, it's still boring with or without alcohol. Likewise, a great night out with friends is fun with or without booze. You don't need alcohol to have fun, and the best thing is that you get to remember what a great time you had the next day. You also have so much more energy and motivation to do things that you find yourself involved in countless new activities and wondering where you ever found the time to fit drinking into your life.

2. Alcohol cures my anxiety or depression. You may have used alcohol to self-medicate for depression or anxiety, and fear that if you quit it will become worse. The fact is that alcohol often exacerbates anxiety and depression to whole new levels. When I quit drinking, I found that within a few months, the dark clouds which had hung over me for years started to clear and were replaced by sunny, happy skies. My anxiety has never come back and I truly believe that alcohol was the fuel to its fire.

3. If I can't have my usual alcoholic drink, what the hell am I going to drink instead? I liked to have a drink in my hand when I sat down and relaxed in the evening. I'm not keen on the word 'habit', but it was exactly that. I, therefore, needed to replace the wine with something else, and was amazed to discover a huge range of wonderful zero-alcohol drinks. Exploring them has been so much fun. These days I always have a lovely, botanical zero-alcohol drink close to hand, so why not try some for yourself? I know that finding a new go-to drink has helped to fill the void for hundreds of people who have successfully quit alcohol.

4. What if I have withdrawal symptoms and cravings when I stop alcohol? This might happen, but within 10 to 14 days of quitting drinking, your body will have rid itself of any trace of alcohol. There will be no physical cravings after this time. Any urges to drink will only be in your mind, and as time goes by, they'll become less and less frequent. However, it's important to learn how to deal with cravings and urges to drink, both in the early stages and as you go further on the sober journey, so please be prepared. If you are concerned about withdrawal symptoms please seek medical advice.

5. If I do stop drinking alcohol it won't last. If you don't try, you'll never know. The chances are that you'll love the incredible changes to your body, mind, and relationships so much that you'll wonder why you didn't quit years ago. Make sure you surround yourself with the right support to stand a real chance of long-term success.

6. I'm genuinely scared that I can't stop drinking. This is how I felt too – I drank wine every single day for over twenty years. As I've mentioned, the key for me was changing my mindset about alcohol, and once I'd settled the internal conflict about it, it became insignificant to me. I believe that anyone can take a one-month break from drink, and if you spend this time educating yourself and working on your mindset there's every chance that by the end of the month, you'll never look back.

7. All my friends drink. It can feel tough when drinking is an integral part of what you and your friends do together, but you have to put yourself first. A true friend will be supportive and understand why you're doing this; they won't judge you. So talk to them, and hopefully, you will find another shoulder to lean on and more accountability. That said, I did have a couple of friendships that were purely based on alcohol and from which I've drifted away.

8. I have a big wedding, event, or party coming up. You might be wondering how you'll get through it if you stop drinking, and that's understandable. My advice here depends on when the event is. If you haven't stopped drinking yet and it's just around the corner, it may be worth waiting until it's out of the way before you put the bottle down. However, if it's months away, I would be confident that you'll have been sober for long enough to feel sufficiently resilient to cope with just about any function.

9. Drinking helps me sleep. You might be worrying that if you quit alcohol you'll be awake all night. In fact, the opposite is true: alcohol might knock you out for a few hours but it doesn't give you a restful night of sleep. Although the first week of not drinking can result in restless nights, you'll soon settle down and start to enjoy the kind of deep sleep that you probably haven't experienced since you were a child. There's also the bonus of waking up with no hangover and feeling ready to take on the day when you spring out of bed (with no boozy breath)!

10. Drinking makes me happy and feel relaxed. It doesn't – it makes you forget your problems for a few hours, which it then serves back to you in high definition the next morning (often when you have a banging headache). You also think you're funnier and happier when you're drunk, but from a sober perspective, you'll see that drunk people are often obnoxious, loud, and repetitive. Only when I quit alcohol did I feel true happiness and become relaxed and at peace in my life. It was something for which I'd been searching for years, and I discovered that the answer was in the bottle, but that it meant putting it down forever.

Conclusion

It's time to take action.

As you go forward on this journey, I want you to reach for this book whenever you're faced with a new challenge. If you're heading off on your first holiday or attending your first wedding without drinking, for instance, simply jump to the relevant chapter, get your journal out, and see what there is to learn. You can arm yourself with the right tactics for just about anything that comes up in your life. Even if something catches you off guard, pause for a moment, and before you do anything hasty, take a minute to read the relevant part of this book and *then* make a decision.

What I would also like you to do

If you haven't already quit drinking, I would like you to make some firm commitments to yourself. Pull out your journal and write down the following statements, which must be honest and true for you.

1. The first one should be: *'I refuse to put alcohol before [whatever or whoever is most important to me] ever again.'*

To complete it, make a list of the things you will not compromise on; you need to make an absolute and real promise to yourself. My statements were:

'I will never again put alcohol before my daughter.'
'I will never again put alcohol before my wife.'
'I will never again put alcohol before my mental health.'

This agreement with yourself is not open to compromise, so please be totally honest about the areas of your life in which alcohol is no longer allowed to come first. You need to mean what you say, and intend to stick to it without question.

2. The second statement I want you to make is: *'I know I can cut alcohol out of my life for XX weeks.'*

You need to fill in the XX with the number of weeks that you know you can happily commit to not drinking. I only want you to write down what you *know* you'll stick to, so please don't over-promise. As a guide, it should be possible for you to commit to at least four weeks. If you don't feel you can do that then it may be sensible for you to seek medical advice or consider working one-to-one with an alcohol coach.

During the period of time you commit to not drinking, I want you to explore how you feel and the changes you notice. I'd like you to journal every day and become inquisitive about it all. There might be highs and there will probably be a few lows; make sure you refer to the chapters in this book that deal with whatever comes up, especially if you feel triggered to drink. I'd also suggest joining the online Alcohol Experiment and using it as another support tool from your first day onwards.

3. I want you to make a further commitment to yourself by writing down this statement: *'If I do decide to drink during the alcohol-free period I've committed to, I'll make a firm and true commitment to avoid drink for a further XX weeks.'*

Again, fill in the XX with the number of weeks you'll commit to; this should be at least two weeks more than the original promise you made. The point of this second extended period is that you know there's a self-imposed penalty if you don't see through the original obligation you gave yourself.

4. Next, I'd like you to make a fourth and final statement: *'Once I've completed my promised period without drinking, I'll reward myself with XX.'*

Here you need to replace XX with a wonderful treat; spa days and fancy restaurants are my favourites. The point of this reward is to help you stay focused and motivated as you move through your time without drinking.

If you're happy to do so, I'd love for you to tell at least one other person what you're doing. Ideally, it would be your spouse, partner, or a close friend – someone who'll be supportive and encourage you in your venture.

Now put the commitments in your line of sight. A great option is to write them on a brightly coloured piece of card and stick it on the fridge so they serve as a daily reminder of the positive actions you're taking. Or if you'd like to keep them private, you could have them on your phone or in your journal (but the more often you see them the better).

When you've reached the end of your commitment period

Finally, after you've completed the period of commitment you've made and you're organising your treat, I'd like you to do one last thing for me. Reflect on what you've written down in your journal: look at the changes that have happened and explore how you feel now compared to when you were drinking. Is your life starting to feel better? Are you feeling happier and more positive? Do you feel more motivated? Do you have more energy? Then, after you've dug deep into what's changed, answer this question:

'Do I need alcohol in my life any longer?'

If the answer is no, you have two options. You can either make a firm promise never to go back to drinking (and this is when you can write your divorce letter to booze if you wish – I love it when members of the *Be Sober* group share theirs, so if you feel happy to do the same, I look forward to seeing it). Or you can commit to an extended period without alcohol to see how it feels as you go forward. At the end of this, you should complete this process as many times as you need, making the periods increasingly longer. The chances are that you'll reach a point at which you simply decide you don't need or want alcohol in your life any more.

If your answer is yes (and I hope it isn't), then it's likely that you believe alcohol is still providing you with some kind of benefit: your mindset hasn't fully shifted. I would urge you to write down what you think drinking is providing you with, and explore those beliefs in close detail. Then pause and look at your beliefs with an investigative and inquisitive nature. Do they really hold true? As part of this, you can return to the chapters of this book that relate to your beliefs, and re-start the education process by reaching out to online support groups and using online tutorials and blogs.

You may not have a complete mindset shift the first time around, but if you've experienced any positive changes at all you'll know you're starting to travel down the right path. You just need to keep putting in a little more work to get yourself where you need to be. Try not to become frustrated or angry if you haven't transformed as quickly or as much as you hoped; be gentle with yourself and go with the flow. But whatever you do, please do keep moving forward. With self-love, ongoing learning, and support, I'm confident you'll reach a place of happiness and peace.

The path to freedom is never a straight one, but it really is worth the walk.

Resources you may find useful

Below are some of the resources I used on my own journey to alcohol freedom, and I invite you to make full use of them as well.

Books

This Naked Mind: Control Alcohol by Annie Grace

The Sober Diaries: How one woman stopped drinking and started living by Clare Pooley

The Unexpected Joy of Being Sober: Discovering a happy, healthy, wealthy alcohol-free life by Catherine Grey

Kick The Drink… Easily! by Jason Vale

The Alcohol Experiment: 30 days to take control, cut down, or give up for good by Annie Grace

Alcohol Explained by William Porter

Websites

www.besober.co.uk – my own blog with articles and information to help you on the sober journey. Here you can also join the *Be Sober* Facebook group.

www.thealcoholexperiment.com – a free 30-day programme to help you change your relationship with alcohol.

www.joinclubsoda.com – Club Soda is a mindful drinking movement. Visit their website to start changing your thinking about drinking.

www.thisnakedmind.com – Annie Grace shares the very best tips, advice, and resources to help anyone who wants to explore their drinking habits and make a positive change.

www.bigsobriety.com - Val Cashman is a This Naked Mind coach working with people who aim to own their badass sobriety.

www.sobersenorita.com – Kelly Fitzgerald Junco shares powerful content to help anyone who wants to be the true version of themselves and explore sobriety in more depth.

www.miraclesarebrewing.com – Carly Benson writes about her adventures in life and sobriety. Carly is a certified recovery coach and yoga teacher specialising in sobriety and spirituality.

About the author

For over two decades, Simon Chapple was a heavy drinker, enduring daily hangovers, carrying out regretful behaviour, and suffering from a lack of motivation. Somehow, he still managed to build a successful business and run 15 marathons, but he was never truly happy and didn't feel like he was anywhere near the best version of himself. He knew something was missing in his life but he couldn't put his finger on exactly what it was. Finally, it came to him: His love affair with red wine had become toxic and was no longer serving him in a positive way.

This was the first of many steps towards finding the key to unlock a life of freedom from alcohol. By the end of it, he'd found complete peace, happiness, and joy for the first time since he was a child.

Because the changes Simon experienced were so life-changing, it became his mission to raise awareness of the dangers of alcohol, and more importantly, the benefits an alcohol-free life can bring.

Simon is the founder of Be Sober, one of the largest and fastest-growing online 'quit drinking' communities in the world. If you haven't already joined the Be Sober movement you can do so for free right now by visiting www.besober.co.uk

Simon is also a certified alcohol coach and has helped thousands of people explore and change their relationship with alcohol for the long term. He's spoken at live events to help educate and inspire people who are wondering what a life without alcohol might look like for them.

He's written this book to help anyone who's concerned about their own relationship with alcohol, and thinking about making a change. To do this he's drawn on his considerable life experience, and the experiences of those he's helped, in order to provide real-world advice and tactics that can be used to make a positive change.

Simon lives in the UK with his wife, daughter, and two cats.

Join the alcohol-free movement at: www.besober.co.uk
Reach out: info@besober.co.uk

Acknowledgements

When I was in the tight grip of alcohol, I would never even have thought about writing a book, but here it is. All that newfound energy and motivation that returned after I quit drove me to achieve something I didn't think was possible. My goal for this book is to continue to spread the word that an alcohol-free life really is the pathway to achieving what you want in life and becoming the best version of yourself.

I could never have completed this project without the support of my wife Michelle. She encouraged me from day one and has held my hand through the highs and lows, both on the journey to alcohol freedom and the challenges that came up when writing and publishing this book. She has always been kind, non-judgmental and ensured that I stayed on the right path. Without her, I would never be where I am today. Michelle, this book is dedicated to you.

Writing this book felt similar to quitting drinking at times. There were some tough challenges and points when I wondered if I would ever get to where I wanted to be. But I stuck with it, I put the work in and kept going because I knew it was what I wanted and I wasn't going to give up.

To Robyn Chapple, my daughter. You are a shining light in my life who never ceases to amaze me. You make me smile every day and I am very proud to call myself your dad. Who needs alcohol with a daughter like you.

To Annie Grace, if it wasn't for you I would still be drinking wine every day and this book would never exist, your work changed my life. Thank you from the bottom of my heart for all the help, advice and opportunities you have given me. You are the leader of a global revolution that I am proud to be part of. You really are an inspiration and I will never forget everything you have done for me.

To Scott Pinyard, what you don't know about alcohol coaching isn't worth knowing. Thank you for sharing your knowledge, being patient with me and helping me to become a better person. You have helped change the lives of so many people and I am honoured to be able to call you my mentor.

To Ginny Carter, you helped me create this book and worked tirelessly with me to make my dream a reality. I couldn't have done this without you, thank you.

To Heather Truman and Katya Lamb. Thank you for all the time and effort you put into helping run the Be Sober Facebook Group. You give up your free time to help make it one of the most incredible alcohol-free communities on the internet and I can't thank you enough for all you do.

Finally, to all the members of the various sober groups I work in. You are all inspirational and I feel so privileged that I am able to be part of your personal journeys to alcohol freedom. You are all sober rebels!

Disclaimer: This book expresses the opinions of the author. It is not a replacement for professional medical advice. If you're physically addicted to alcohol, or experiencing severe withdrawal symptoms, such as shaking, tremors, hallucinations, or any other side-effects that cause you concern, please visit your doctor and get medical advice.

The Sober Survival Guide - How to Free Yourself From Alcohol Forever by Simon Chapple
Copyright © 2019

Published by Elevator Digital Ltd

Paperback ISBN: 978-1-9162500-9-3

eBook ISBN: 978-1-9162500-2-4

Printed in Poland
by Amazon Fulfillment
Poland Sp. z o.o., Wrocław

60885037R00106